RINGS AND IDEALS

By
NEAL HENRY McCOY
Professor of Mathematics, Smith College

THE
CARUS MATHEMATICAL MONOGRAPHS

Published by

THE MATHEMATICAL ASSOCIATION OF AMERICA

———

THE CARUS MATHEMATICAL MONOGRAPHS are an expression of the desire of Mrs. Mary Hegeler Carus, and of her son, Dr. Edward H. Carus, to contribute to the dissemination of mathematical knowledge by making accessible at nominal cost a series of expository presentations of the best thoughts and keenest researches in pure and applied mathematics. The publication of the first four of these monographs was made possible by a notable gift to the Mathematical Association of America by Mrs. Carus as sole trustee of the Edward C. Hegeler Trust Fund. The sales from these have resulted in the Carus Monograph Fund, and the Mathematical Association has used this as a revolving book fund to publish the succeeding monographs.

The expositions of mathematical subjects which the monographs contain are set forth in a manner comprehensible not only to teachers and students specializing in mathematics, but also to scientific workers in other fields, and especially to the wide circle of thoughtful people who, having a moderate acquaintance with elementary mathematics, wish to extend their knowledge without prolonged and critical study of the mathematical journals and treatises. The scope of this series includes also historical and biographical monographs.

---

*The following books in this series
have been published to date:*

RINGS AND IDEALS

By

NEAL H. McCOY
Professor of Mathematics
Smith College

Published by
THE MATHEMATICAL ASSOCIATION OF AMERICA

Published August 1948
Second Impression October 1956

PRINTED IN THE UNITED STATES OF AMERICA
George Banta Company, Inc. Menasha, Wisconsin

PREFACE

During the last twenty or thirty years abstract algebra has been developed in very rapid fashion by an increasingly large number of research workers. In fact, the general methods and most fundamental results of the theory have become of considerable interest to mathematicians generally, even though their primary interests may lie in other directions. The purpose of this monograph is to present an introduction to that branch of abstract algebra having to do with the theory of rings, with some emphasis on the role of ideals in the theory.

Except for a knowledge of certain fundamental theorems about determinants which is assumed in Chapter VIII, and at one point in Chapter VII, the book is almost entirely self-contained. Of course, the reader must have a certain amount of "mathematical maturity" in order to understand the illustrative examples, and also to grasp the significance of the abstract approach. However, in so far as formal technique is concerned, little more than the elements of algebra are presupposed.

The first four chapters treat those fundamental concepts and results which are essential in a more advanced study of any branch of ring theory. The rest of the monograph deals with somewhat more specialized results which, however, are of fairly wide interest and application. Naturally, many other topics of equal significance have had to be omitted simply because of space limitations. For the most part, material has been chosen which does not require any finiteness assumptions on the rings considered—the concept of a chain condition is not even mentioned until late in the last chapter!

Chapter V consists primarily of an exposition of Krull's results on prime ideals in a commutative ring. Since no finiteness conditions are imposed, it is necessary to use transfinite methods in establishing the existence of the prime ideals. Actually, Zorn's Maximum Principle is all that is required, and this is carefully stated and illustrated at an appropriate point in the chapter.

An exposition of the theory of subdirect sums of rings is given in Chapter VI, together with a brief introduction to the Jacobson radical of a ring. Chapter VII is concerned with Boolean rings and with a number of algebraic generalizations of these rings. In particular, Stone's theorem on the representation of any Boolean ring as a ring of subsets of some set is obtained quite easily from results of the preceding chapter.

The theory of matrices with elements in a commutative ring is the subject of Chapter VIII. Obviously, in one brief chapter it is impossible to give a comprehensive account of the theory. However, this short exposition has been included partly because of the generality of the approach, and partly because the material furnishes illustrations of a number of fundamental methods in the elementary theory of rings. This chapter is independent of the two preceding chapters. Finally, Chapter IX is an introduction to the study of primary ideals in a commutative ring. It ends with a short discussion of Noetherian rings (rings with ascending chain condition) and a brief section on algebraic manifolds.

Since a considerable part of the material of this monograph has not previously appeared in book form, it has seemed desirable to give somewhat more complete references than might otherwise be the case. Accordingly, at the end of each chapter there appears a list of references to supplement the general material of the chapter, and also occasional source references to some of the more specific results which are not adequately treated in the available treatises. The bibliography at the back of the book is by no means complete; for the most part, only those items have been included to which reference is made at some point in the text.

It would be impossible to list here all the books and articles to which I am indebted. However, it may not be out of order to mention van der Waerden's *Moderne Algebra* which has played an important role in the development of widespread interest in abstract algebra. In so far as content is concerned, much of the first four chapters of this monograph, and a small part of the last, cover material which is included in van der Waerden's treatise.

I am greatly indebted to Professors Bailey Brown, R. E. Johnson, and Saunders MacLane, who have read the entire manuscript and made many valuable suggestions. In particular, Professor Brown has taken an active interest in this project from its very inception and I have profited much by many discussions with him. Not only has he read the manuscript in all its versions in an unusually careful and critical manner, but he also has been of invaluable assistance in reading the proofs.

NEAL HENRY McCOY

Northampton, Mass.
August 22, 1947

TABLE OF CONTENTS

CHAPTER I

DEFINITIONS AND FUNDAMENTAL PROPERTIES

1. **Definition of a ring.** Let us consider a set R of elements $a, b, c, \cdots$, such that for arbitrary elements a and b of R there is a uniquely defined *sum* $a + b$ and *product* ab (sometimes written as $a \cdot b$) which are also elements of R. The words *addition* and *multiplication*, as in the ordinary usage of elementary algebra, will be respectively associated with the operations of forming a sum, or a product, of elements of R. Such a set is said to be a *ring* if addition and multiplication have the five properties listed below, it being assumed that a, b, and c are arbitrary elements of R, either distinct or identical:

P_1. $a + (b + c) = (a + b) + c$ (*associative law of addition*);

P_2. $a + b = b + a$ (*commutative law of addition*);

P_3. *The equation $a + x = b$ has a solution x in R*;

P_4. $a(bc) = (ab)c$ (*associative law of multiplication*);

P_5. $a(b + c) = ab + ac$, $(b + c)a = ba + ca$ (*distributive laws*).

The importance of the concept of *ring* follows primarily from the fact that there are so many important mathematical systems of quite different types which are rings according to the above definition. Naturally, what they all have in common are the properties used in the definition of a ring, together with any properties which are logical consequences of these. Later on, we shall deduce a number of these logical consequences and thus obtain properties which all rings must have. However, before proceeding further in this direction, we pause to give a number of

1

examples which will help to clarify the concepts involved and also to illustrate something of the variety of mathematical systems which are rings.

2. **Examples of rings.** In order to give an example of a ring, it is necessary to exhibit a set of elements and also to give definitions of addition and multiplication of these elements which satisfy the five properties listed above. In some of the illustrations to be given presently, the actual verification of these properties will be left to the reader since they follow by straightforward calculations, or are already well known.

In the first place, it is clear that many of the number systems of ordinary algebra are rings with respect to the usual definitions of addition and multiplication. Thus we have *the ring of even integers* (positive, negative and zero), *the ring of all integers, the ring of rational numbers, the ring of real numbers, the ring of complex numbers.* It will be noticed that each of these rings is contained in each of the ones following it, and is therefore said to be a *subring* of each following one. It is also readily verified that the set of all numbers of the form $a + b\sqrt{2}$, where a and b are rational, is a ring; as is also the set of all polynomials in a real variable, with real coefficients. Furthermore, since the sum and product of continuous functions are also continuous, it is easily seen that the class of all real functions which are continuous in an arbitrary fixed interval is a ring. It may also be shown that the set of all power series in a real variable, which converge in some interval, is a ring with respect to the usual definitions of addition and multiplication of power series.

The ring of all integers is of such fundamental importance and will be referred to so frequently that it will be convenient to have a consistent notation for this ring.

Hereafter, the letter I will be used to denote the ring of all integers.

In addition to these most familiar rings, we now give, in somewhat more detail, a few additional examples. As a matter of fact, most of the rings to be presented will be considered in later chapters and hence, at the present time, no attempt will be made to indicate the importance or significance of these examples. At this point, our primary purpose is to give some indication of the great variety of rings, and also to have a body of examples from which to obtain illustrations of the various results to be established in later sections.

Example 1. *The ring I_n of integers modulo n*, where n is any positive integer. The elements of this ring are the symbols $0'$, $1'$, $2'$, $\cdots$, $(n - 1)'$. If a' and b' are any of these elements, we define $a' + b'$ to be r', where r is the least nonnegative remainder when the ordinary sum of a and b is divided by n. Similarly, by $a'b'$ we mean s', where s is the least nonnegative remainder when the ordinary product of a and b is divided by n. Thus, by way of illustration, the ring I_6 of integers modulo 6 consists of the six elements $0'$, $1'$, $2'$, $3'$, $4'$, $5'$. If the ordinary sum of 4 and 5 is divided by 6, the remainder is 3, hence in this ring, $4' + 5' = 3'$. Similarly, $2' + 4' = 0'$, $2' \cdot 4' = 2'$, $2' \cdot 3' = 0'$, and so on.

To prove that I_n is actually a ring, it is necessary to use the well-known fact that in the division of any integer by n, the least nonnegative remainder is unique. In fact, it will be clear that this property is essential for the definitions of addition and multiplication given above. We shall prove the associative law of addition as an illustration of the method which may be used.

Let a', b', c' be any elements of I_n . If

$$(1) \qquad a + b = q_1 n + r_1 \, ,$$

where $0 \leq r_1 < n$, then, by definition of addition in I_n,

$$a' + b' = r_1' .$$

Hence $(a' + b') + c' = r_1' + c'$. To compute this, we write

$$(2) \qquad r_1 + c = q_2 n + r_2 ,$$

where $0 \leq r_2 < n$, and thus

$$(a' + b') + c' = r_2' .$$

However, if we substitute the value of r_1 from (2) into equation (1), we see that

$$a + b + c = (q_1 + q_2)n + r_2 ,$$

and thus r_2 is the least nonnegative remainder in the division of $a + b + c$ by n. A similar calculation will show that

$$a' + (b' + c') = r_2' ,$$

and thus

$$(a' + b') + c' = a' + (b' + c'),$$

as desired.

Properties P_4 and P_5 follow by this same type of calculation, while P_2 is obvious. To prove P_3, we observe that if a' and b' are any elements of I_n, the equation $a' + x = b'$ has the solution $x = (b - a)'$ if $b \geq a$, and the solution $x = (n + b - a)'$ if $b < a$.

We may remark that the method by which the ring I_n is constructed from the ring of integers is a special case of an important procedure to be explained fully in Chapter III.

Example 2. *The ring B of all subsets of $\mathcal{I}$*, where $\mathcal{I}$ denotes the unit interval on the x-axis, that is, $\mathcal{I}$ is the set of all points with abscissa x such that $0 \leq x \leq 1$. A set of points of $\mathcal{I}$ is naturally called a *subset* of $\mathcal{I}$. For example, any single point of $\mathcal{I}$ is a subset of $\mathcal{I}$, as is also the set of all points with abscissa x such that $0 \leq x \leq \frac{1}{2}$. These are simple illustrations, but it is clear that there is a great variety of subsets. According to our definition, it will be seen that the set of *all* points of $\mathcal{I}$ is itself a subset of $\mathcal{I}$. It will also be convenient to consider that the *void set*, that is, the set which contains no points, is a subset of $\mathcal{I}$. This will serve to simplify various statements which otherwise would not always be true without exception.

If now B is the set of *all* subsets of $\mathcal{I}$, including the void set, we shall presently make B into a ring by suitable definitions of addition and multiplication. It may be emphasized that an *element* of B is a *subset* of $\mathcal{I}$.

Let a and b be any two elements of B. With reference to a and b, the points of $\mathcal{I}$ may be distributed into the following mutually exclusive classes, certain ones of which may happen to contain no points: (1) points in neither a nor b, (2) points in a but not in b, (3) points in b but not in a, (4) points in both a and b. This fact may be exhibited in a convenient but purely symbolic way as indicated in Fig. 1. Here a is represented by the points inside circle a, and b by the points inside circle b. The classes (1), (2), (3), and (4) are respectively represented by the regions marked 1, 2, 3, and 4 in the figure.

We are now ready to define addition and multiplication in B. By ab we mean the *intersection* of a and b, that is, the set of all points in both a and b. In Fig. 1, ab is thus exhibited as the set of points in region 4. We define $a + b$ to be the set of all points in a or in b *but not in both*. Thus, in Fig. 1, regions 2 and 3 together represent $a + b$.

It is obvious that if a and b have no points in common, ab is the void set. Hence the product of two subsets of $\mathcal{I}$ would not always be a subset of $\mathcal{I}$ if it were not for our agreement that the void set is to be so considered.

Properties P_2 and P_4 are almost obvious, but we shall

indicate a method of proof of P_1. Let a, b, c be three elements of B. With reference to these elements, the points of $\mathcal{I}$ may be separated into eight mutually exclusive classes, as indicated in Fig. 2. Here a, b, c are represented symbolically by the points inside the circles marked a, b, and c respectively. We shall not enumerate the eight classes but may point out, by way of illustration, that region 2

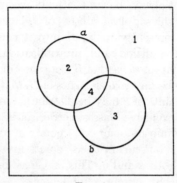

Fig. 1

represents the set of all points which are in a but in neither b nor c.

Now $a + b$ is represented by regions 2, 3, 5, and 6. Since c is made up of regions 4, 5, 6, and 8, it is clear that $(a + b) + c$ is represented by regions 2, 3, 4, and 8. This graphical representation then suggests that we may characterize $(a + b) + c$ as the subset of $\mathcal{I}$ which consists of all points in exactly one of the sets a, b, c, together with those in all three. This can clearly be proved in a purely logical way without reference to the diagram, but the diagram does give a visual indication of the logical steps involved. The reader may now verify that $a + (b + c)$ can be characterized in exactly the same way, and this will establish the associative law of addition. Property P_5 can be proved by the same general method and we therefore omit the proof.

For the equation, $a + x = b$, we obtain a solution by taking x to be $a + b$ as defined above, hence P_3 is true.

It will be noted that the ring B has some remarkable properties which have not been true for the rings previously mentioned. Thus, for example, in this ring $a \cdot a = a$ for *every* element a. Rings with this property will be discussed in detail in Chapter VII. It is obvious that, in this

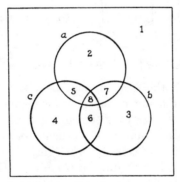

Fig. 2

example, any set $\mathfrak{M}$ of points may be used in place of the interval $\mathcal{I}$, and thus one may obtain *the ring of all subsets of the arbitrary set* $\mathfrak{M}$.

Example 3. *The ring of all finite subsets of an arbitrary set* $\mathfrak{M}$. For concreteness, let $\mathfrak{M}$ be the interval $\mathcal{I}$ of the preceding example. It was shown above that the set of *all* subsets of $\mathcal{I}$ is a ring under suitable definitions of addition and multiplication. With these same definitions, it is clear that if a and b contain only a finite number of points the same is true of both $a + b$ and ab. It follows readily that the set of all finite subsets of $\mathcal{I}$ is also a ring, naturally a *subring* of the ring of all subsets of $\mathcal{I}$.

Example 4. *The ring of all real matrices of order* 2. This ring consists of all symbols of the form

$$\begin{bmatrix} e_{11} & e_{12} \\ e_{21} & e_{22} \end{bmatrix},$$

where e_{11}, e_{12}, e_{21}, e_{22} are real numbers, with addition and multiplication defined respectively as follows:

$$\begin{bmatrix} e_{11} & e_{12} \\ e_{21} & e_{22} \end{bmatrix} + \begin{bmatrix} f_{11} & f_{12} \\ f_{21} & f_{22} \end{bmatrix} = \begin{bmatrix} e_{11} + f_{11} & e_{12} + f_{12} \\ e_{21} + f_{21} & e_{22} + f_{22} \end{bmatrix},$$

$$\begin{bmatrix} e_{11} & e_{12} \\ e_{21} & e_{22} \end{bmatrix} \begin{bmatrix} f_{11} & f_{12} \\ f_{21} & f_{22} \end{bmatrix} = \begin{bmatrix} e_{11}f_{11} + e_{12}f_{21} & e_{11}f_{12} + e_{12}f_{22} \\ e_{21}f_{11} + e_{22}f_{21} & e_{21}f_{12} + e_{22}f_{22} \end{bmatrix}$$

The proof that this is a ring may be left to the reader.

In a similar manner, one may define the ring of real matrices of order n (n rows and columns) and also one may replace the real numbers by elements of other number systems—in fact, by elements of any ring. Rings of matrices will be discussed more fully in Chapter VIII.

Before proceeding, we point out that in all examples preceding this last one, the order of the factors in a product is immaterial. However, this is not always the case in the ring of real matrices of order 2. Thus, for example,

$$\begin{bmatrix} 0 & 1 \\ 0 & 0 \end{bmatrix} \begin{bmatrix} 0 & 0 \\ 1 & 0 \end{bmatrix} = \begin{bmatrix} 1 & 0 \\ 0 & 0 \end{bmatrix},$$

while

$$\begin{bmatrix} 0 & 0 \\ 1 & 0 \end{bmatrix} \begin{bmatrix} 0 & 1 \\ 0 & 0 \end{bmatrix} = \begin{bmatrix} 0 & 0 \\ 0 & 1 \end{bmatrix}.$$

Example 5. *The ring of real quaternions.* As elements of this ring we use all symbols

$$(e_1, \ e_2, \ e_3, \ e_4),$$

where e_1, e_2, e_3, e_4 are real numbers. Addition and multiplication are defined respectively as follows:

$$(e_1, \ e_2, \ e_3, \ e_4) + (f_1, f_2, f_3, f_4) = (e_1 + f_1,$$

$$e_2 + f_2, \ e_3 + f_3, \ e_4 + f_4),$$

$$(e_1, e_2, e_3, e_4)(f_1, f_2, f_3, f_4) = (e_1f_1 - e_2f_2 - e_3f_3 - e_4f_4,$$

$$e_1f_2 + e_2f_1 + e_3f_4 - e_4f_3, \ e_1f_3 - e_2f_4 + e_3f_1 + e_4f_2,$$

$$e_1f_4 + e_2f_3 - e_3f_2 + e_4f_1).$$

We may remark that a different, but logically equivalent, definition of this ring is to be found in many texts on algebra. However, for the purpose of illustration, the present definition is simpler and entirely satisfactory.

It is fairly obvious that the properties of addition are satisfied, and P_4 and P_5 may be verified by straightforward but detailed calculations.

The ring of real quaternions also has the property that the order of the factors in a product is important. For example, we have

$$(0, \ 1, \ 0, \ 0)(0, \ 0, \ 1, \ 0) = (0, \ 0, \ 0, \ 1),$$

$$(0, \ 0, \ 1, \ 0)(0, \ 1, \ 0, \ 0) = (0, \ 0, \ 0, \ -1).$$

In any ring R, if a and b are elements such that $ab = ba$, it may be said that either of these elements is *commutative with* the other. If R has the property that a is commutative with b for *every* choice of a and b, R is said to be a *commutative ring*; otherwise it is a *noncommutative ring*. Thus all the examples of rings given above, with the exception of the last two, are commutative rings; while the last two are noncommutative rings. It is clear that for *commutative* rings either of the distributive laws P_5 is a consequence of the other.

3. **Properties of addition.** We now return to a further consideration of the defining properties of a ring. The properties P_1, P_2, and P_3 are precisely the properties which define an *Abelian* (commutative) *group*, and the fundamental properties of addition in a ring are simply properties of such groups. However, we do not assume a familiarity with these concepts but shall derive the required properties in some detail.

Let a and b be elements, distinct or identical, of the arbitrary ring R. By P_3, there exist elements n and n' of R such that

$$a + n = a,$$

and $$b + n' = b.$$

Likewise there exist elements x and y such that

$$a + x = n',$$

and $$b + y = n.$$

It follows, therefore, by using P_1 and P_2, that

$$n = b + y = y + b = y + (b + n') = (y + b) + n'$$
$$= (b + y) + n' = n + n',$$

and

$$n' = a + x = x + a = x + (a + n) = (x + a) + n$$
$$= (a + x) + n = n' + n = n + n'.$$

This shows that $n = n'$, and hence that there exists a *unique* element n of R with the property that

$$a + n = n + a = a$$

for *every* element a of R. Henceforth, this element n will be denoted by the familiar symbol 0 and called the *zero element,* or simply the *zero,* of R. Any other element is naturally said to be a *nonzero* element. Thus every ring has a zero, and clearly a ring also has nonzero elements unless it happens that the ring has only one element.

The reader will have no difficulty in identifying the zeros of the rings previously mentioned. As illustrations, we may note that in the ring of all subsets of $\mathcal{I}$, the void set is the zero; while the zero of the ring of real matrices of order 2 is the matrix

$$\begin{bmatrix} 0 & 0 \\ 0 & 0 \end{bmatrix}.$$

In the ring of real functions continuous in some interval, the zero is the function which vanishes identically.

One of the defining properties of a ring states that there exists an element x such that

$$a + x = b.$$

It is now easy to show that this equation has a *unique* solution. Suppose that also

$$a + y = b,$$

and that t is an element such that

$$a + t = 0.$$

It follows that

$$x = x + 0 = x + (a + t) = (x + a) + t = b + t$$
$$= (a + y) + t = (a + t) + y = 0 + y = y,$$

and the solution is therefore unique.

The unique solution of

$$a + x = 0$$

we henceforth denote by $-a$, and write $b + (-a)$ as $b - a$. Since $-a + a = 0$, it follows readily that

$$-(-a) = a.$$

Inasmuch as $a - b$ is really $a + (-b)$, various laws of *subtraction* follow from those of addition. Thus, for example, the following may be readily verified:

$$-(a + b) = -a - b,$$
$$-(a - b) = -a + b,$$
$$(a - b) - c = (a - c) - b.$$

At this point, it may be well to make a few remarks about the associative law of addition. Inasmuch as

$$a + (b + c) = (a + b) + c,$$

it is customary not to distinguish between these and to write simply

$$a + b + c,$$

without use of parentheses. It is then quite clear that

$$(a + b + c) + d = (a + b) + (c + d) = a + (b + c + d),$$

that is, the sum of four elements is independent of the way in which parentheses may be introduced, and hence such a sum can be conveniently and unambiguously written as

$$a + b + c + d$$

It is now fairly obvious that a similar result holds for any finite sum, and we shall use this fact without further mention. A rigorous proof can be given by the method of finite induction.

It goes, almost without saying, that these remarks also apply to the associative law of multiplication, that is, in a product of a finite number of elements it is unnecessary to use parentheses inasmuch as the product is independent of the way in which the elements may be associated. Furthermore, it is easy to show that the distributive laws as stated in P_5 imply that

$$a(b_1 + b_2 + \cdots + b_n) = ab_1 + ab_2 + \cdots + ab_n ,$$

and

$$(b_1 + b_2 + \cdots + b_n)a = b_1a + b_2a + \cdots + b_na ,$$

where n is any positive integer.

From the results so far obtained it will be noted that, in any ring, the combining of elements by addition and subtraction is done precisely as in the number systems of elementary algebra. We shall see below that the situation is quite different when we come to consider multiplication.

4. **Further fundamental properties.** If a and b are arbitrary elements of the ring R, it follows from one of the distributive laws that

$$a(b + 0) = ab + a \cdot 0.$$

But since $b + 0 = b$, we see, by substitution, that also

$$a(b + 0) = ab.$$

Thus

$$ab \cdot + \quad a \cdot 0 = ab,$$

from which it follows that $a \cdot 0 = 0$. In like manner, it may be shown that $0 \cdot a = 0$, and thus *a product is zero if one of the factors is zero*. The converse of this is not, however, generally true as will be shown presently. If it happens that there exists a nonzero element b such that $ab = 0$, or a nonzero element c such that $ca = 0$, a is said to be a *divisor of zero.* According to this definition, 0 is always a divisor of zero except in the trivial case in which 0 is the only element of R. A nonzero divisor of zero may be conveniently called a *proper* divisor of zero. Since the ordinary number systems have no proper divisors of zero, the possible presence of such elements in a ring means that certain familiar rules of calculation are not valid in a general ring.

As illustrations of the notion of divisor of zero, let us refer to some of the examples of rings given previously. In the ring I_6, we saw that $2' \cdot 3' = 0'$, and thus $2'$ and $3'$ are divisors of zero. It will be seen that $4'$ is also a divisor of zero in this ring, since $4' \cdot 3' = 0'$. The ring of all subsets of $\mathcal{I}$ consists almost entirely of divisors of zero—in fact, the element consisting of the entire interval $\mathcal{I}$ is the only element which is not a divisor of zero. This follows easily from the observation that if a is any proper subset of $\mathcal{I}$, and b is any set of points of $\mathcal{I}$ not in a, then $ab = 0$. In the ring of all *finite* subsets of $\mathcal{I}$, every element is a divisor of zero. It is also easy to exhibit divisors of zero in the ring of real matrices of order 2; for example,

$$\begin{bmatrix} 0 & 1 \\ 0 & 0 \end{bmatrix} \begin{bmatrix} 0 & 2 \\ 0 & 0 \end{bmatrix} = \begin{bmatrix} 0 & 0 \\ 0 & 0 \end{bmatrix}.$$

It will be shown below that the ring of real quaternions has no proper divisors of zero. However, these examples should make it clear that proper divisors of zero occur frequently and are by no means exceptional.

We now consider some additional properties of general rings. Since

$$a(-b) + ab = a(-b + b) = a \cdot 0 = 0,$$

it follows that

$$a(-b) = -(ab).$$

In like manner, it is easy to verify in turn the following:

$$(-a)b = -(ab),$$

$$(-a)(-b) = -[a(-b)] = -[-(ab)] = ab,$$

$$a(b - c) = ab + a(-c) = ab - ac,$$

$$(b - c)a = ba - ca.$$

In any ring, *if a is not a divisor of zero, either of the equations*,

$$ax = ay, \qquad xa = ya,$$

implies that $x = y$. As proof, we see that these equations are respectively equivalent to the equations,

$$a(x - y) = 0, \quad (x - y)a = 0,$$

and if a is not a divisor of zero it follows that $x - y = 0$, or $x = y$. However, if a is a divisor of zero, it may well happen that $ax = ay$ with $x \neq y$. Thus, for example, in the ring I_6 we have $2' \cdot 2' = 2' \cdot 5'$ with $2' \neq 5'$.

A commutative ring without proper divisors of zero is often called an *integral domain*. The name comes from the fact that any integral domain has a number of properties in common with the ring of integers and, in turn, the ring of integers is one of the simplest examples of an integral domain. In an integral domain, if $a \neq 0$, the equation $ax = ay$ always implies that $x = y$.

If a ring R has an element e such that

$$ea = ae = a$$

for *every* element a of R, e is called a *unit element* of R. If f is also a unit element of R, it follows that

$$e = ef = f,$$

and therefore if a ring has a unit element, it is *unique*. If, as is usually the case, a ring has at least two elements, it has at least one nonzero element and hence the unit element is different from zero. The unit element of a ring, if it exists, will frequently be denoted by e, or simply by 1 if no confusion can arise from the use of this familiar symbol. It is clear from some of the examples previously given that a ring need not have a unit element. For example, the ring of even integers has no unit element, and neither does the ring of all finite subsets of $\mathcal{I}$. The unit element of the ring of all subsets of $\mathcal{I}$ is the set consisting of the entire interval $\mathcal{I}$. It is also easily verified that the unit element of the ring of real matrices of order 2 is the matrix

$$\begin{bmatrix} 1 & 0 \\ 0 & 1 \end{bmatrix},$$

while the unit element of the ring of real quaternions is the element $(1, 0, 0, 0)$.

If the ring R has a unit element e, and a and b are elements of R such that

$$ab = ba = e,$$

then either of these elements is said to be an *inverse* of the other. We shall now show that if a has an inverse, it is *unique*. If b and c are inverses of a, it follows that

$$ac = ab,$$

and if this equation be multiplied on the left by b, we get $ec = eb$, or $c = b$. The unique inverse of a, if it exists, is usually denoted by a^{-1}.

In any ring, if an element a has an inverse, a can not be a divisor of zero. For if $ab = 0$, and we multiply by a^{-1} on the left, we see that

$$a^{-1}ab = eb = b = 0.$$

Similarly, $ba = 0$ implies that $b = 0$, so a is not a divisor of zero.

If a is any element of R, we may denote $a \cdot a$ by a^2, $a \cdot a \cdot a$ by a^3, and so on. Likewise, if a has an inverse a^{-1}, we denote $(a^{-1})^n$ by a^{-n}, and agree that $a^0 = e$. It is easy to verify that the following laws of exponents always hold for positive integers m, n:

$$a^m \cdot a^n = a^{m+n},$$
$$(a^m)^n = a^{mn}.$$

If a has an inverse, these hold for arbitrary (including negative and zero) integers m, n. If R happens to be a commutative ring, we see also that

$$(ab)^m = a^m b^m,$$

but this is not generally true for noncommutative rings. Thus, for example,

$$(ab)^2 = abab,$$

and this may well not be identical with $a^2 b^2$ unless $ba = ab$.

If a and b have inverses, we see that

$$(ab)(b^{-1}a^{-1}) = aea^{-1} = aa^{-1} = e,$$

and likewise it may be shown that

$$(b^{-1}a^{-1})(ab) = e.$$

Hence ab has an inverse and

$$(ab)^{-1} = b^{-1}a^{-1}.$$

Thus the inverse of a product is the product of the inverses in the opposite order. Naturally, in a commutative ring no attention need be paid to the order of multiplication.

If a is any element of R it will be convenient to denote $a + a$ by $2a$ and, more generally,

$$a + a + \cdots + a \qquad (m \text{ summands})$$

by ma (or by $m \cdot a$), m being any positive integer. If 0 is the zero integer, we define the symbol $0a$ to be the zero element of R. If we also define $(-m)a$ to be $-(ma)$, we may verify the following for all integers m, n (positive, negative or zero):

$$(m + n)a = ma + na,$$
$$m(na) = (mn)a,$$
$$m(a + b) = ma + mb,$$
$$m(ab) = (ma)b = a(mb).$$

It should be observed that ma is not necessarily expressible as the product of two elements of R. For example, in the ring of even integers, we have

$$3 \cdot 2 = 2 + 2 + 2,$$

and 3 is not an element of the ring. This situation can not occur, however, if R has a unit element. For if e is the unit element of R, we see that

$$ma = m(ea) = (me)a,$$

and ma may be considered as the product of two elements of R, namely, me and a. Because of this fact, if R has a unit element, ma may be considered either as

$$a + a + \cdots + a \qquad (m \text{ summands})$$

or as $(me)a$. As a matter of fact, the symbol 1 is frequently used to denote the unit element of a ring, in which case m may be used in the sense of $m \cdot 1$ and is therefore actually an element of the ring.

This concludes our discussion of the most elementary and fundamental properties of rings. The results of this and the preceding section may be approximately summed up by saying that most of the rules for combining elements of a ring by addition and multiplication are the familiar rules of elementary algebra. The main points of difference arise from the possible presence of divisors of zero in a ring, and also from the fact that in a ring multiplication need not be commutative. Additional, but perhaps less striking, differences arise from the fact that a ring may or may not have a unit element and, even if it has a unit element, not all elements necessarily have inverses.

5. **Division rings and fields.** A ring D is said to be a *division ring* if it has more than one element and if for every nonzero element a of D the equation

$$ax = b$$

has a solution for arbitrary b in D. In the literature, the term *skew field* (or *sfield*) is sometimes used to denote a division ring. We shall presently give some examples but first we prove the following fundamental result:

THEOREM 1. *A division ring D has a unit element, and every nonzero element has an inverse.*

As a first step in the proof, we show that a division ring has no proper divisor of zero, that is, the vanishing of a product implies that one of the factors is zero. To show this, suppose that c and d are nonzero elements of D. By definition of division ring, there is an element x such that $cx = d$ and also an element y such that $dy = x$. Hence

$$cdy = cx = d.$$

Since $d \neq 0$, it follows that $cd \neq 0$ and thus a product of nonzero elements can not be zero.

We next prove that D has a unit element. Let a be a fixed nonzero element of D, and e an element of D, necessarily different from zero, such that

$$ae = a.$$

From this, it follows that $ae^2 = ae$, and hence $e^2 = e$ since a is not a divisor of zero.

Now if t is any element of D, we see that

$$(t - te)e = 0, \quad e(t - et) = 0.$$

Hence

$$te = et = t$$

for *every* element t of D, that is, e is the unit element of D.

It is now easy to prove that every nonzero element a has an inverse. By the definition of division ring, there is an element x such that

$$ax = e,$$

and clearly x is different from zero. It follows that

$$(xa - e)x = x(ax) - ex = xe - ex = 0,$$

and hence $xa - e = 0$, or $xa = e$. Thus x is the inverse a^{-1} of a, and the proof of the theorem is completed.

If $a \neq 0$, a is not a divisor of zero, and thus $ax = ay$ implies that $x = y$. Hence the equation $ax = b$, which has a solution by the definition of division ring, actually has a *unique* solution. Furthermore, this solution has the simple form

$$x = a^{-1}b,$$

since this clearly satisfies the equation. From this, it is clear that in order to prove that a ring with more than one element is a division ring it is sufficient to show that the ring has a unit element and that every nonzero element has an inverse.

COROLLARY. *In a division ring, the equation*

$$ya = b \qquad\qquad (a \neq 0)$$

always has a unique solution, namely, $y = ba^{-1}$.

Thus, although our definition only requires that equations of the form $ax = b$ be solvable, it is true that the equations $ya = b$ are also solvable.

We now show that the ring of real quaternions is a division ring. Let $a = (e_1, e_2, e_3, e_4)$ be any real quaternion other than the zero. This means that some $e_i \neq 0$, and therefore the real number

$$g = e_1^2 + e_2^2 + e_3^2 + e_4^2$$

is different from zero. The unit element of the ring of real quaternions is $(1, 0, 0, 0)$, and it is readily verified that

$$a^{-1} = (e_1/g, -e_2/g, -e_3/g, -e_4/g).$$

This is sufficient to show that we have a division ring.

A commutative division ring is called a *field*. Since multiplication of quaternions is not necessarily commutative, the ring of real quaternions is an example of a division ring which is not a field. As most familiar examples of fields, we may mention the field of rational numbers, the field of real numbers and the field of complex numbers. It is also easy to verify that the ring of all numbers of the form $a + b\sqrt{2}$, where a and b are rational, is a field.

As an example of a field of a different nature than those mentioned above, let us consider the ring of integers modulo 5, which consists of the five elements

$$0', \quad 1', \quad 2', \quad 3', \quad 4',$$

with addition and multiplication as defined in Example 1 of §2. Clearly, $1'$ is the unit element of this ring, and the zero is the element $0'$. That each nonzero element has an inverse follows from the easily verified relations,

$$1' \cdot 1' = 1', \quad 2' \cdot 3' = 1', \quad 4' \cdot 4' = 1'.$$

This shows that I_5 is actually a field. It is also an interesting fact, which is readily verified, that if a is any nonzero element of I_5,

$$a^4 = 1',$$

and thus the equation,

$$x^5 = x,$$

is satisfied by *every* element of the field, including zero.

THEOREM 2. *The ring I_n of integers modulo n is a field if and only if n is a prime.*

If n is not a prime, we have $n = n_1 n_2$ $(n_1 > 1, n_2 > 1)$ and thus, by definition of multiplication in I_n, $n_1' n_2' = 0'$ with $n_1' \neq 0'$, $n_2' \neq 0'$. Since a field can have no proper divisors of zero, this proves one part of the theorem.

Suppose, now, that p is a prime and consider the ring I_p whose elements are

$$0', 1', 2', \cdots, (p-1)'.$$

It is readily seen that I_p contains no proper divisor of zero, for a product of integers is divisible by the prime p only if one of the factors is divisible by p. Let a be any fixed nonzero element of I_p and consider the set of all elements of I_p of the form ay, where y runs over the nonzero elements of I_p. Since there are no proper divisors of zero, these elements are all distinct, are $p - 1$ in number, hence must be, in some order, precisely the nonzero elements of I_p. Thus the equation $ax = b$ has a solution for every nonzero b in I_p. If $b = 0$, it has the obvious solution $x = 0$; hence I_p is a field.

We now show that the equation

$$x^p = x$$

is satisfied by *every* element of I_p, thus generalizing a statement made earlier for the special case in which $p = 5$. To show this, we let a be any nonzero element, take the product of all elements ay, where y is a nonzero element of I_p, and use the fact that this must give us the product of all nonzero elements of I_p. That is,

$$1' \cdot 2' \cdots (p-1)' a^{p-1} = 1' \cdot 2' \cdots (p-1)'.$$

Since there are no proper divisors of zero, this implies that $a^{p-1} = 1'$, and therefore $x^p = x$ is satisfied by every element, including the zero.

COROLLARY. *If m is a positive integer less than the prime p, there exists a positive integer n less than p such that*

$$mn = 1 + kp,$$

for some nonnegative integer k.

This follows at once from the observation that m' has an inverse n' in the field I_p, and thus 1 is the remainder in the division of mn by p, while k is the quotient in this division.

A field with a finite number of elements is called a *finite field* or a *Galois field* [after the famous French mathematician, Evariste Galois (1811–1832)]. We have therefore shown that there exists a finite field of p elements, where p is any prime. Although we have exhibited some finite fields, it will be noted that the ring of real quaternions which is a division ring, but not a field, has an infinite number of elements. Indeed, any such example must have an infinite number of elements in view of a well-known theorem of Wedderburn which states that *any division ring with a finite number of elements is neces-*

sarily a field. In other words, provided one assumes that the number of elements is finite, the commutativity of multiplication is a logical consequence of the defining properties of a division ring. The proof of this fact will not be given here.

The finite field I_p has the following interesting property which has not been explicitly mentioned. If a is any element of I_p,

$$pa = a + a + \cdots + a \quad (p \text{ summands})$$

is always zero. The field is therefore said to have the *characteristic p*. More generally, if for an arbitrary ring R, there exists a positive integer n such that $na = 0$ for *every* element a of R, the least such n is called the *characteristic* of R, and R is also said to have *positive characteristic*. If no such positive integer exists, R is said to have *characteristic* 0. The familiar number systems of algebra obviously have characteristic 0, while the ring of all subsets of $\mathcal{I}$ has characteristic 2.

If R has a unit element e, it is readily seen that the characteristic of R is the least positive integer n such that $ne = 0$, if there exists such an n; otherwise the characteristic is 0. For if $ne = 0$, it follows that

$$na = n(ea) = (ne)a = 0 \cdot a = 0,$$

for every element a of R.

If R has a unit element e and positive characteristic n, it is clear that the elements

$$0, \ e, \ 2e, \ \cdots, \ (n \ - \ 1)e$$

are all distinct. Furthermore, *every* integral multiple of e, that is, every element of the form ke, where k is an arbitrary integer, is equal to some element of this set. This follows from the fact that k can be expressed in the form

$$k = qn + r \qquad (0 \leq r < n),$$

and hence

$$ke = qne + re = re.$$

From this calculation, it also follows that $ke = 0$ if and only if $r = 0$, in other words, if and only if k is divisible by n.

If a ring with unit element and with no proper divisors of zero has positive characteristic, it is easy to see that the characteristic must be a prime. For example, such a ring can not have characteristic 6, for $6e = 0$ would imply that $(2e)(3e) = 0$ and one of these factors must be zero, thus violating the assumption that 6 is the least positive integer n such that $ne = 0$. It is obvious how to give a general proof by this same method and thus, in particular, *the characteristic of any field must be either 0 or a prime.*

If the ring R has prime characteristic p, it is not difficult to show that p is the least positive integer n such that $na = 0$, where a is *any* nonzero element of the ring. For if m is a positive integer less than p such that $ma = 0$, it follows from the Corollary to Theorem 2 that there exist integers s, t, such that

$$1 = ms + tp,$$

and thus

$$a = msa + tpa = 0.$$

We shall now prove one more theorem about finite fields, as follows:

THEOREM 3. *If a finite field has n elements, n is of the form p^m, where m is a positive integer and p the (prime) characteristic of the field.*

Let F be a finite field with n elements, and let the unit element of F be e. Since F has only n elements, not all the elements

$$e, 2e, 3e, \cdots, (n + 1)e$$

can be different, and hence there exist two different positive integers l_1, l_2, such that $l_1 e = l_2 e$. Thus $(l_1 - l_2)e = 0$ and F has positive characteristic, which must be a prime p. It follows that the p elements

$$ke \qquad (k = 0, 1, \cdots, p - 1),$$

are distinct, and that *all* integral multiples of e are in this set. If there are no other elements in F, the proof is completed with $m = 1$. If there is an element a of F which is not an integral multiple of e, we shall show that the p^2 elements of the form,

$$k_1 e + k_2 a \quad (k_1, k_2 = 0, 1, \cdots, p - 1),$$

are all distinct. Suppose that two elements of this form are equal, say,

$$k_1 e + k_2 a = k_1' e + k_2' a,$$

and let us assume that $k_2 \neq k_2'$. Suppose, for definiteness, that $k_2 > k_2'$, and let us write

$$(k_2 - k_2')a = (k_1' - k_1)e.$$

Now $0 < k_2 - k_2' < p$, and hence, by the Corollary to Theorem 2, there exist integers r, s such that

$$r(k_2 - k_2') = 1 + sp.$$

Multiplication of the equation preceding this one by r shows that

$$a = r(k_1' - k_1)e,$$

since $pa = 0$. This violates our assumption that a is not an integral multiple of e, and hence we must have $k_2' = k_2$. It then follows that $(k_1' - k_1)e = 0$, and since k_1 and k_1' are less than the characteristic p, this implies that $k_1 = k_1'$, that is, our p^2 elements are distinct.

Now if there is an element b of F not expressible in the form $k_1 e + k_2 a$, a similar argument will show that all p^3 elements,

$$k_1 e + k_2 a + k_3 b \quad (k_1, k_2, k_3 = 0, 1, \cdots, p - 1),$$

are distinct. This process may be continued and, since F has only a finite number of elements, must finally come to an end after a certain number m of steps. It follows that F has p^m elements, as was to be proved.

It is also true, although we shall omit the proof, that if p is any prime and m any positive integer, there *does exist* a field with p^m elements.

This very brief introduction to the theory of fields will be sufficient for our purposes but it should be remarked that fields play an important role in modern algebraic theories. The interested reader will have no difficulty in finding detailed accounts in any text on modern algebra.

6. **Equivalence relations.** There is one further concept which may be appropriately introduced at this point. In the preceding, we have used continually the notion of *equality*. Thus, $a = b$ has been tacitly interpreted to mean that a and b are identical elements of R. However, a careful analysis of the use we have made of this concept will show that only the following three properties of equality have actually been used:

(i) *For every a of R, $a = a$;*
(ii) *If $a = b$, then $b = a$;*
(iii) *If $a = b$ and $b = c$, then $a = c$.*

In combination with the ring operations, we have also

made use of the fact that sums (products) of *equal* elements are *equal*.

These remarks suggest that, in the definition of a ring, one might use, instead of identity, some other *equality* having these properties. This point will come up again in Chapter III. In the meantime, we proceed to formulate more fully the ideas involved and introduce a convenient terminology.

Let $\mathcal{K}$ be an arbitrary set of elements a, b, c, $\cdots$ (not necessarily elements of a ring), and suppose there is a relation $\sim$ defined on pairs of elements of the set such that, for arbitrary elements a, b of $\mathcal{K}$, $a \sim b$ is either true or false. Such a relation is called an *equivalence relation* if it has the following three properties:

(i) *For every a of $\mathcal{K}$, $a \sim a$ (reflexive law)*;

(ii) *If $a \sim b$, then $b \sim a$ (law of symmetry)*;

(iii) *If $a \sim b$ and $b \sim c$, then $a \sim c$ (transitive law)*.

Thus, equality, in the sense of identity, is one example of an equivalence relation. In plane geometry, both congruence of triangles and similarity of triangles are further illustrations of this concept. Another important example, which we proceed to explain in detail, is that of congruence modulo n in the ring of integers. For concreteness, let $n = 6$, although these ideas apply as well to arbitrary n. It will be recalled that

$$a \equiv b \text{ modulo } 6,$$

which is read, "a is congruent to b, modulo 6," means that $a - b$ is divisible by 6. Throughout the rest of this section, the word "congruence" will be used to mean "congruence modulo 6." It will be readily verified that congruence satisfies the conditions specified above and is therefore an equivalence relation defined on the integers. It is clear that no one of the integers,

$$0,\ 1,\ 2,\ 3,\ 4,\ 5,$$

is congruent to another of this set, but that *every* integer is congruent to some one of this set. Thus, congruence has the property that it separates the class of all integers into the following disjoined subclasses:

$$\cdots,\ -12,\ -6,\ 0,\ \ 6,\ 12,\ \cdots,$$
$$\cdots,\ -11,\ -5,\ 1,\ \ 7,\ 13,\ \cdots,$$
$$\cdots,\ -10,\ -4,\ 2,\ \ 8,\ 14,\ \cdots,$$
$$\cdots,\ \ -9,\ -3,\ 3,\ \ 9,\ 15,\ \cdots,$$
$$\cdots,\ \ -8,\ -2,\ 4,\ 10,\ 16,\ \cdots,$$
$$\cdots,\ \ -7,\ -1,\ 5,\ 11,\ 17,\ \cdots,$$

in which all the integers in any row are congruent to each other but not to an integer in any other row. If n is any integer, let $\bar{n}$ denote the set of all integers in the above scheme which are in the row with n. Then the six classes,

$$\bar{0},\ \bar{1},\ \bar{2},\ \bar{3},\ \bar{4},\ \bar{5},$$

may be called the *equivalence classes* of the integers modulo 6. We shall return to a further consideration of this example in Chapter III.

It will now be almost obvious that an arbitrary equivalence relation on any set $\mathcal{K}$ will serve to separate $\mathcal{K}$ into a set of subclasses (generally not finite in number), the elements of any subclass being the set of all elements of $\mathcal{K}$ equivalent to any member of the subclass. These *equivalence classes* have the following properties:

(i) *Every element of $\mathcal{K}$ is in some class,*

(ii) *No two different classes have an element in common.*

Conversely, it is readily verified that any set of subclasses of elements of $\mathcal{K}$ having these properties can be used to *define* an equivalence relation on $\mathcal{K}$ by agreeing that two elements are to be considered as equivalent if and only if they belong to the same subclass.

REFERENCES*

Albert [1], Chapters I, II, VII; Birkhoff and MacLane [1], Chapters I, II, XIII, XIV, XV; Bourbaki [1], §1–5,8; Dubreil [1], Chapters I(B), IV(D); MacDuffee [2], Chapters III, V; van der Waerden [1], Chapters III, V.

The ring of all subsets of $\mathcal{J}$ was apparently first discussed in Fraenkel [1]; see also Stone [1].

Several proofs are given in Wedderburn [1] that a finite division ring is a field.

Expositions of the theory of finite fields will be found in most of the texts listed above, and also in Dickson [1].

---

* The numbers in square brackets refer to the bibliography at the end of the monograph.

CHAPTER II

POLYNOMIAL RINGS

7. Definitions and simple properties. In the preceding chapter, we gave a number of examples of rings and used them to illustrate various points of the theory. We now introduce another important class of rings.

Let R be an arbitrary ring, x an arbitrary symbol or *indeterminate* (not an element of R), and consider all finite expressions of the type

$$(3) \quad f(x) = a_0x^0 + a_1x^1 + a_2x^2 + \cdots + a_nx^n,$$

where a_i is an element of R $(i = 0, 1, \cdots, n)$. Such an expression may be called a *polynomial* in x with coefficients in R. It is assumed that the symbol x is commutative with all elements of R, that is, that ax is not to be distinguished from xa.

If $f(x)$ is the polynomial (3), and

$$(4) \quad g(x) = b_0x^0 + b_1x^1 + b_2x^2 + \cdots + b_mx^m$$

is another polynomial, we may define the sum of $f(x)$ and $g(x)$ to be the polynomial

$$(a_0 + b_0)x^0 + (a_1 + b_1)x^1 + (a_2 + b_2)x^2 + \cdots,$$

obtained by adding coefficients of corresponding powers of x in $f(x)$ and in $g(x)$. A power of x which does not appear in $f(x)$ (or in $g(x)$) is considered to have the coefficient zero. It is clear that, according to this definition, a polynomial is actually the sum of its monomial constituents, that is, $f(x)$ is the sum of the special polynomials a_ix^i $(i = 0, 1, \cdots, n)$.

We now define $f(x)g(x)$ to be the polynomial

$$a_0 b_0 x^0 + (a_1 b_0 + a_0 b_1)x^1 + (a_2 b_0 + a_1 b_1 + a_0 b_2)x^2 + \cdots ,$$

obtained by using the same formal rules as in multiplying ordinary real polynomials in a real variable, except that we are careful to write the a's on the left in each term since R may not be commutative.

Two polynomials are considered as equal if and only if the coefficients of each power of x are the same in both polynomials. With respect to the definitions of addition and multiplication just given, the set of all polynomials in x with coefficients in R forms a ring. The properties of addition follow almost at once from the corresponding properties for R. Let us consider the associative law of multiplication, and to this end let

$$h(x) = c_0 x^0 + c_1 x^1 + \cdots + c_k x^k$$

be a third polynomial. The coefficient of any power of x, say x^i, in $[f(x)g(x)]h(x)$ is the sum of all expressions of the form $(a_\alpha b_\beta)c_\gamma$, where $\alpha + \beta + \gamma = i$. Similarly, the coefficient of x^i in $f(x)[g(x)h(x)]$ is the sum of all terms of the form $a_\alpha(b_\beta c_\gamma)$, where $\alpha + \beta + \gamma = i$. However, these two sums are equal by the associative law of multiplication for R. Thus

$$[f(x)g(x)]h(x) = f(x)[g(x)h(x)],$$

which is the associative law of multiplication. The reader will have no difficulty in similarly verifying the distributive laws. Thus, we have a ring which will henceforth be denoted by $R[x]$. It is clear that the ring $R[x]$ is a commutative ring if and only if R is a commutative ring.

It is almost obvious that we may replace ax^0, a an element of R, by a alone, that is, that we may omit the symbol x^0 entirely.* The elements of R are then actually

* A precise formulation of the general principle involved will be found in Theorem 20.

elements of $R[x]$, so that $R[x]$ contains R as a subring. Accordingly, we shall henceforth identify ax^0 with a, write x in place of x^1, and therefore express our polynomials in the more familiar form,

$$f(x) = a_0 + a_1x + \cdots + a_nx^n.$$

It will sometimes be convenient to refer to a_0 as the *constant term* of $f(x)$.

In a polynomial, the exponent of the highest power of x which has a nonzero coefficient is called the *degree* of the polynomial, and this coefficient is the *leading coefficient*. In particular, the polynomials of degree 0 are just the nonzero elements of R. The zero polynomial has no degree according to our definition. If R has a unit element, a polynomial whose leading coefficient is this unit element may be conveniently called a *monic* polynomial.

From the definition of $R[x]$ it is clear that x itself is not an element of $R[x]$. However, if R has a unit element e, we may identify x with ex. This is justified since $(ex)^i = ex^i$, and therefore $a(ex)^i = ax^i$. Hence, in this most important case, we may consider x to be an element of $R[x]$, and thus ax may be considered as the actual product of the elements a and x of the ring $R[x]$.

Let $f(x)$ and $g(x)$ be given by (3) and (4) respectively, and let us assume that $a_n \neq 0$, $b_m \neq 0$, so that $f(x)$ is of degree n and $g(x)$ is of degree m. The coefficient of x^{n+m} in the product of $f(x)$ and $g(x)$ is a_nb_m ; and clearly no higher power of x can possibly occur with nonzero coefficient. Hence the degree of $f(x)g(x)$ can not be greater than the sum of the degrees of $f(x)$ and $g(x)$, and will be equal to this sum if $a_nb_m \neq 0$. If either a_n or b_m is not a divisor of zero in R, $f(x)g(x)$ has exactly the degree $n + m$. Thus, *if R has no proper divisors of zero, the degree of a product of two nonzero polynomials is equal to the sum of the degrees of the two polynomials*. In this case, therefore, $R[x]$

has no proper divisors of zero. It follows that $R[x]$ is an integral domain if and only if R is an integral domain. It is also an obvious consequence of the above remarks that for completely arbitrary R, *a monic polynomial can not be a divisor of zero in $R[x]$.*

As a simple illustration of what may happen if R has proper divisors of zero, let R be the ring I_{12} of integers modulo 12. If $f(x) = 4'x^2 + 2'x + 6'$, $g(x) = 3'x^2 + 2'x$, we see that

$$f(x)g(x) = 2'x^3 + 10'x^2,$$

and thus the degree of the product is less than the sum of the degrees of the factors. As a matter of fact, $f(x)$ is itself a divisor of zero since $f(x)(6'x + 6') = 0'$ or, for that matter, $6'f(x) = 0'$. This is an illustration of the next theorem which completely characterizes the divisors of zero in $R[x]$, where R is a commutative ring.

THEOREM 4. *Let $f(x)$ be an element of $R[x]$, where R is a commutative ring. Then $f(x)$ is a divisor of zero in $R[x]$ if and only if there exists a nonzero element c of R such that $cf(x) = 0$.*

Before indicating the method of proof of this theorem, we may point out that the theorem merely states that a polynomial $f(x)$ is a divisor of zero in $R[x]$ if and only if there is a nonzero element c of R such that the product of c by *every* coefficient in $f(x)$ is zero. In particular, if the coefficient of *some* power of x in $f(x)$ is not a divisor of zero in R, $f(x)$ is not a divisor of zero in $R[x]$.

The sufficiency of the condition is obvious, as is also the necessity in case $f(x)$ is zero or of degree 0. Hence we may assume that $f(x)$ has positive degree. The method of proof will be sufficiently illustrated by a special case which we proceed to discuss in detail. Let

$$f(x) = a_0 + a_1x + a_2x^2 + a_3x^3 \qquad (a_3 \neq 0),$$

and

$$g(x) = b_0 + b_1x + b_2x^2 \qquad (b_2 \neq 0),$$

be such that $g(x)f(x) = 0$. We shall first show that *there is a nonzero polynomial $g'(x)$, of degree less than the degree of $g(x)$, such that $g'(x)f(x) = 0$.*

Since $g(x)f(x) = 0$, the coefficient of x^5 in this product must certainly be zero, that is, we must have $a_3b_2 = 0$. Now

$$[a_3g(x)]f(x) = 0,$$

while $a_3g(x) = a_3(b_0 + b_1x)$ is certainly zero or of degree less than two. Hence, if $a_3g(x) \neq 0$, we may use it as the $g'(x)$ which we seek. Suppose, then, that $a_3g(x) = 0$, that is, that

$$a_3b_0 = a_3b_1 = a_3b_2 = 0.$$

This means that

$$g(x)f(x) = (b_0 + b_1x + b_2x^2)(a_0 + a_1x + a_2x^2) = 0,$$

from which we now see that $b_2a_2 = 0$. Hence

$$[a_2g(x)]f(x) = [a_2(b_0 + b_1x)]f(x) = 0,$$

and we can, as above, take $a_2(b_0 + b_1x)$ as the required $g'(x)$ unless it happens that $a_2g(x) = 0$. Hence we may assume that $a_2g(x) = 0$, and thus

$$g(x)f(x) = (b_0 + b_1x + b_2x^2)(a_0 + a_1x) = 0,$$

from which it follows that $a_1b_2 = 0$. This implies that

$$a_1g(x)f(x) = a_1(b_0 + b_1x)f(x) = 0,$$

and we can take $g'(x) = a_1g(x)$ unless $a_1g(x) = 0$. If $a_1g(x) = 0$, we see that

$$g(x)f(x) = a_0g(x) = 0.$$

We have thus found a $g'(x)$ unless it happens that

$$a_3g(x) = a_2g(x) = a_1g(x) = a_0g(x) = 0.$$

However, if these are all zero, it follows that

$$a_3b_2 = a_2b_2 = a_1b_2 = a_0b_2 = 0,$$

that is, $b_2f(x) = 0$, and $b_2 \neq 0$ is of degree 0. Thus, in every case, there exists a $g'(x)$ of degree less than that of $g(x)$ such that $g'(x)f(x) = 0$.

If $g'(x)$ is of degree 1, a repétition of the argument by which we passed from $g(x)$ to $g'(x)$ will show that there exists a nonzero element c of R such that $cf(x) = 0$.

A general proof of this theorem, following the above line of reasoning, can be given without difficulty although the notation is naturally somewhat more complicated. It will be clear that the proof actually involves a process of induction on the degree of $g(x)$.

8. Division transformation. Factor and remainder theorems.

We shall now prove the following theorem, which is an extension of the familiar *division transformation* for real or complex polynomials:

THEOREM 5. *Let R be an arbitrary ring with unit element, and let*

$$f(x) = a_nx^n + a_{n-1}x^{n-1} + \cdots + a_0 \quad (a_n \neq 0),$$

and

$$g(x) = b_mx^m + b_{m-1}x^{m-1} + \cdots + b_0 \quad (b_m \neq 0),$$

be elements of $R[x]$, it being assumed that b_m has an inverse b_m^{-1} in R. Then there exist unique elements $q(x)$, $p(x)$, $r(x)$, $s(x)$ of $R[x]$ such that

$$(5) \qquad f(x) = q(x)g(x) + r(x),$$

and

(6) $$f(x) = g(x)p(x) + s(x),$$

where $r(x)$ and $s(x)$ are zero or of degree less than m, and $q(x)$ and $p(x)$ are zero or of degree $n - m \geq 0$.

We shall first show the *existence*, and return to the proof of *uniqueness* a little later. If $n < m$, it is clear that (5) and (6) are satisfied by choosing $q(x) = p(x) = 0$, $r(x) = s(x) = f(x)$; hence we assume that $n \geq m$. Let us consider the polynomial

$$f_1(x) = f(x) - [a_n b_m^{-1} x^{n-m}]g(x),$$

in which the coefficient of x^n is

$$a_n - a_n b_m^{-1} b_m = 0.$$

We note further that $a_n b_m^{-1} x^{n-m}$ is actually of degree $n - m$ since $a_n \neq 0$, and b_m^{-1} is not a divisor of zero since it has an inverse. If the degree of $f_1(x)$ is less than m, we may clearly take

$$q(x) = a_n b_m^{-1} x^{n-m}, \; r(x) = f_1(x).$$

If, however, the degree of $f_1(x)$ is $k \geq m$, and the coefficient of x^k in $f_1(x)$ is $c \neq 0$, we can repeat the above process and consider

$$\begin{aligned} f_2(x) &= f_1(x) - cb_m^{-1} x^{k-m} g(x) \\ &= f(x) - [a_n b_m^{-1} x^{n-m} + cb_m^{-1} x^{k-m}]g(x), \end{aligned}$$

whose degree is less than k. If the degree of $f_2(x)$ is less than m, we may choose

$$q(x) = a_n b_m^{-1} x^{n-m} + cb_m^{-1} x^{k-m}, \; r(x) = f_2(x).$$

If, however, the degree of $f_2(x)$ is greater than m, or equal to m, we may repeat the above process and after a finite number of steps we must find an $r(x)$ and a $q(x)$ which satisfy equation (5) and meet the stated requirements as to degrees.

The existence of $p(x)$ and $s(x)$ follows by the same argument except that in place of the $f_1(x)$ used above, we use

$$f'(x) = f(x) - g(x)[b_m^{-1} a_n x^{n-m}],$$

and make a similar modification at later steps in the construction.

We shall now prove the uniqueness of $q(x)$ and $r(x)$. Suppose, in addition to (5), that we have

$$f(x) = q_1(x)g(x) + r_1(x),$$

where $r_1(x)$ is zero or of degree less than m, and $q_1(x)$ is zero or of degree $n - m \geq 0$. Then

(7) $$[q(x) - q_1(x)]g(x) = r_1(x) - r(x).$$

Suppose that $r_1(x) - r(x)$ is of degree l_1, where $0 \leq l_1 < m$. Then $q(x) - q_1(x)$ is not zero and has degree $l_2 \geq 0$. But since b_m is not a divisor of zero, the degree of the left side of (7) must be $m + l_2$, which is impossible since the degree of the right side is less than m. Hence $r_1(x) - r(x)$ can have no degree, that is, we must have $r_1(x) = r(x)$. It then follows that also $q(x) = q_1(x)$ since $g(x)$ is not a divisor of zero. The proof of the uniqueness of $p(x)$ and $s(x)$ will be omitted since it is entirely analogous to the above.

For convenience, we may call the $r(x)$ of Theorem 5 the *right remainder* in the division of $f(x)$ by $g(x)$; similarly $s(x)$ is the *left remainder* in the division of $f(x)$ by $g(x)$. These clearly coincide in case R is a commutative ring.

If R is any ring, a an element of R, and

(8) $$f(x) = a_n x^n + a_{n-1} x^{n-1} + \cdots + a_0$$

an element of $R[x]$, we define $f_R(a)$ and $f_L(a)$ as follows:

$$f_R(a) = a_n a^n + a_{n-1} a^{n-1} + \cdots + a_0,$$
$$f_L(a) = a^n a_n + a^{n-1} a_{n-1} + \cdots + a_0.$$

Thus $f_R(a)$ and $f_L(a)$ are uniquely defined elements of R. If R is a commutative ring, it is clear that these are equal; otherwise this will not generally be the case. We shall now prove the following *Remainder Theorem:*

THEOREM 6. *If R is a ring with unit element, and a is any element of R, then $f_R(a)$ is the unique right remainder in the division of $f(x)$ by $x - a$, and $f_L(a)$ is the unique left remainder in the division of $f(x)$ by $x - a$.*

The assumption that R has a unit element is essential in order that $x - a$ shall be an element of $R[x]$.

Let

$$f(x) = q(x)(x - a) + r,$$

where r is the unique right remainder in the division of $f(x)$ by $x - a$, according to Theorem 5. Since r is zero or of degree 0, it follows that r is an element of R. If

$$q(x) = q_{n-1} x^{n-1} + q_{n-2} x^{n-2} + \cdots + q_0,$$

a simple calculation will show that

$$f(x) = q_{n-1} x^n + (q_{n-2} - q_{n-1} a) x^{n-1} + \cdots$$
$$+ (q_0 - q_1 a) x - q_0 a + r,$$

and thus

$$f_R(a) = q_{n-1} a^n + (q_{n-2} - q_{n-1} a) a^{n-1} + \cdots$$
$$+ (q_0 - q_1 a) a - q_0 a + r$$
$$= r.$$

The proof for the other case will now be obvious.

If $f(x) = f_1(x)f_2(x)$, where all these polynomials are elements of $R[x]$, we may say that $f_2(x)$ is a *right factor* (or *right divisor*) of $f(x)$, and $f_1(x)$ is a *left factor* (or *left divisor*) of $f(x)$.

THEOREM 7. *If R has a unit element, $f(x)$ has $x - a$ as a right factor if and only if $f_R(a) = 0$. Similarly, $f(x)$ has $x - a$ as a left factor if and only if $f_L(a) = 0$.*

This is obviously an extension of the ordinary Factor Theorem of elementary algebra. The preceding theorem shows that

$$f(x) = q(x)(x - a) + f_R(a),$$

from which it follows that if $f_R(a) = 0$, $x - a$ is a right factor of $f(x)$, and conversely.

We now let R be a *commutative* ring. In this case, $f_R(a)$ and $f_L(a)$ coincide, and we may use the more familiar notation, $f(a)$. Furthermore, if $f(x) = g(x)h(x)$, it is clear that $f(a) = g(a)h(a)$. If $f(a) = 0$, we say that a is a *root* of the equation $f(x) = 0$. In case R has a unit element, it follows from the last theorem that a is a root of this equation if and only if $f(x)$ has $x - a$ as a factor (either right or left, since R is assumed to be commutative).

THEOREM 8. *If R is an integral domain with unit element and $f(x)$ is an element of $R[x]$ of degree n, the equation*

$$(9) \qquad f(x) = 0$$

has not more than n distinct roots in R.

The theorem is obvious in case $n = 0$. We therefore assume that $n > 0$ and suppose that the equation has roots r_1, r_2, $\cdots$, r_n, where these are distinct elements of R. Since $f(r_1) = 0$, it follows that

$$(10) \qquad f(x) = (x - r_1)f_1(x),$$

where $f_1(x)$ is of degree $n - 1$. If we replace x by r_2 in this equation, we get

$$0 = (r_2 - r_1)f_1(r_2).$$

Since $r_1 \neq r_2$ and R has no proper divisors of zero, it follows that $f_1(r_2) = 0$, and hence that

$$f_1(x) = (x - r_2)f_2(x).$$

Thus equation (10) becomes

$$f(x) = (x - r_1)(x - r_2)f_2(x),$$

where $f_2(x)$ is of degree $n - 2$. A continuation of this process shows finally that

$$f(x) = a(x - r_1)(x - r_2) \cdots (x - r_n),$$

where a is a nonzero element of R, actually the leading coefficient of $f(x)$. Now if r is any root of the equation $f(x) = 0$, we have

$$f(r) = a(r - r_1)(r - r_2) \cdots (r - r_n) = 0,$$

from which it follows that r must be one of the r_i since R has no proper divisors of zero. This shows that the equation can have at most n distinct roots.

In this theorem it is essential that R be an integral domain, as otherwise the situation may be quite different. As an extreme case, it is easily verified that in the ring of all subsets of $\mathcal{I}$, as defined in §2, *every* element satisfies the equation $x^2 = x$. This ring is commutative but is not an integral domain since it has many divisors of zero. On the other hand, the ring of real quaternions has no proper divisors of zero but, being noncommutative, is not an integral domain. Furthermore, each of the three quaternions,

$$(0,\ 1,\ 0,\ 0,),\ (0,\ 0,\ 1,\ 0),\ (0,\ 0,\ 0,\ 1),$$

satisfies the quadratic equation $x^2 + 1 = 0$.

9. Polynomials with coefficients in a field. Throughout this section we consider the polynomial ring $F[x]$, where x is an indeterminate and F an arbitrary *field*. Clearly $F[x]$ is commutative and has no proper divisors of zero, in other words, $F[x]$ is an integral domain. In this case, therefore, the degree of a product of nonzero factors is always the sum of the degrees of the factors.

Let $f(x)$ be an element of $F[x]$ of positive degree, and suppose that $f(x)$ has the element $h(x)$ of $F[x]$ as a divisor, that is, that there exists an element $k(x)$ of $F[x]$ such that

$$(11) \qquad f(x) = h(x)k(x).$$

If $h(x)$ and $k(x)$ are of positive degree and have leading coefficients c and d respectively, we may rewrite (11) in the form

$$f(x) = cd[c^{-1}h(x)][d^{-1}k(x)],$$

where $c^{-1}h(x)$ and $d^{-1}k(x)$ are monic polynomials. It is clear, therefore, that in factoring a polynomial we may always choose the factors of positive degree to be monic polynomials.

A monic polynomial $d(x)$ is said to be a *greatest common divisor* (g.c.d.) of the polynomials $f(x)$ and $g(x)$ if (i) $d(x)$ is a common divisor of $f(x)$ and $g(x)$, and (ii) every common divisor of $f(x)$ and $g(x)$ is a divisor of $d(x)$.

THEOREM 9. *Any two polynomials $f(x)$ and $g(x)$, not both zero, of $F[x]$ have a unique g.c.d. which may be characterized as the monic polynomial of minimum degree which can be expressed in the form*

$$(12) \qquad s(x)f(x) + t(x)g(x),$$

where $s(x)$ and $t(x)$ are elements of $F[x]$.

Let us denote by A the set of *all* polynomials of the form (12). Clearly A contains monic polynomials, for if $l(x)$ is any element (12) of A, with leading coefficient b, then $b^{-1}l(x)$ is a monic polynomial, and is in A since

$$b^{-1}l(x) = [b^{-1}s(x)]f(x) + [b^{-1}t(x)]g(x).$$

Now among the elements of A there must exist a polynomial of minimum degree, and furthermore a monic polynomial $d(x)$ of this minimum degree. It is clear that $d(x)$ is unique, for if $d'(x)$ is also monic and of minimum degree in A, then $d(x) - d'(x)$ is in A and is zero or of lower degree than $d(x)$. Because $d(x)$ has minimum degree in A it follows that $d(x) = d'(x)$.

It is now easy to show that $d(x)$ is a g.c.d. of $f(x)$ and $g(x)$. By the division transformation (Theorem 5), we may express $f(x)$ in the form

$$f(x) = q(x)d(x) + r(x),$$

where $r(x)$ is zero or of degree less than the degree of $d(x)$. However, since

$$r(x) = f(x) - q(x)d(x),$$

it is obvious that $r(x)$ is in A and hence, because of the assumption that $d(x)$ has minimum degree in A, it follows that $r(x) = 0$. Thus, $d(x)$ is a divisor of $f(x)$, and in like manner it can be shown that $d(x)$ is also a divisor of $g(x)$. This establishes one of the properties of the greatest common divisor.

Now if $d_1(x)$ is any common divisor of $f(x)$ and $g(x)$, we may write

$$f(x) = d_1(x)f_1(x), \quad g(x) = d_1(x)g_1(x).$$

Furthermore, since $d(x)$ is in A, there exist polynomials

$s_1(x)$, $t_1(x)$ such that

$$
\begin{aligned}
d(x) &= s_1(x)f(x) + t_1(x)g(x) \\
     &= s_1(x)d_1(x)f_1(x) + t_1(x)d_1(x)g_1(x) \\
     &= [s_1(x)f_1(x) + t_1(x)g_1(x)]d_1(x).
\end{aligned}
$$

This shows that any common divisor of $f(x)$ and $g(x)$ is a divisor of $d(x)$, and thus completes the proof that $d(x)$ is a g.c.d. of $f(x)$ and $g(x)$. The uniqueness of the g.c.d. follows from the easily verified fact that if each of two monic polynomials is divisible by the other, they must be identical.

We now turn to a consideration of the factorization of elements of $F[x]$. Let $f(x)$ be an element of $F[x]$ of positive degree. If there exist elements $h(x)$ and $k(x)$ of $F[x]$ of positive degree such that

$$f(x) = h(x)k(x),$$

then $f(x)$ is said to be *reducible;* otherwise $f(x)$ is *irreducible*. It should be emphasized that the concept of reducibility is relative to the given field F. That is, if $f(x)$ is irreducible in $F[x]$, it may very well happen that for some field F_1 containing F, $f(x)$ is reducible as an element of $F_1[x]$. As an illustration, if F is the field of rational numbers and F_1 the field of numbers of the form $a + b\sqrt{2}$, where a and b are rational, the polynomial $x^2 - 2$ is irreducible as an element of $F[x]$ but factors into $(x + \sqrt{2})(x - \sqrt{2})$ as an element of $F_1[x]$. However, at present, we shall restrict attention to a field F and only consider reducibility in $F[x]$. It will be shown later (Theorem 21) that any polynomial of degree greater than one which is irreducible in $F[x]$ is reducible in $F_1[x]$ for suitable choice of the field F_1.

If $f(x)$ is a reducible element of $F[x]$, then the factors $h(x)$ and $k(x)$ of $f(x)$ are both of lower degree than the degree of $f(x)$. If, say, $h(x)$ is reducible, it may be factored into factors of still lower degree. Since a polynomial of the first degree is necessarily irreducible, this process must come to an end, and hence $f(x)$ can eventually be expressed as a product of irreducible factors. Furthermore, the remarks made at the beginning of this section show that these irreducible factors may be taken to be monic. In other words, we may write

$$(13) \qquad f(x) = ap_1(x)p_2(x) \cdots p_r(x),$$

where a is the leading coefficient of $f(x)$ and the $p_i(x)$ are irreducible monic polynomials. We shall presently show that this factorization is unique, except for the order of the factors.

LEMMA. *If $f_1(x)f_2(x)$ is divisible by an irreducible polynomial $p(x)$, then $f_1(x)$ or $f_2(x)$ is divisible by $p(x)$.*

Suppose that $f_1(x)$ is not divisible by $p(x)$. Then, since $p(x)$ is irreducible, the g.c.d. of $f_1(x)$ and $p(x)$ is 1. The preceding theorem then shows that there exist polynomials $s(x)$, $t(x)$, such that

$$1 = s(x)f_1(x) + t(x)p(x),$$

and multiplication by $f_2(x)$ yields

$$f_2(x) = f_2(x)s(x)f_1(x) + f_2(x)t(x)p(x).$$

But, by hypothesis, we have

$$f_1(x)f_2(x) = l(x)p(x),$$

and hence

$$f_2(x) = [s(x)l(x) + t(x)f_2(x)]p(x),$$

that is, $f_2(x)$ is divisible by $p(x)$. This proves the lemma.

Now suppose that, in addition to (13), $f(x)$ can be expressed in the form

$$f(x) = aq_1(x)q_2(x) \cdots q_s(x),$$

where the $q_i(x)$ are irreducible monic polynomials, and hence that

$$p_1(x)p_2(x) \cdots p_r(x) = q_1(x)q_2(x) \cdots q_s(x).$$

Thus the right side is divisible by $p_1(x)$, and an application of the lemma shows that some $q_i(x)$ is divisible by $p_1(x)$. Suppose the notation is so chosen that $q_1(x)$ is divisible by $p_1(x)$. Since these are irreducible monic polynomials it follows that $p_1(x) = q_1(x)$, and hence

$$p_2(x) \cdots p_r(x) = q_2(x) \cdots q_s(x).$$

A repetition of this argument will show finally that $r = s$ and that the $p_i(x)$ are just the $q_i(x)$ in some order. If we express the product of identical irreducible factors as a power of one of them, this result yields the following theorem:

THEOREM 10. *An element $f(x)$ of $F[x]$ of positive degree can be uniquely expressed, except for the order of the factors, in the form*

$$f(x) = a[p_1(x)]^{k_1}[p_2(x)]^{k_2} \cdots [p_j(x)]^{k_j},$$

where a is the leading coefficient of $f(x)$, the $p_i(x)$ are distinct irreducible monic polynomials, and the k_i are positive integers.

10. **Rings of polynomials in several indeterminates.** Let R be an arbitrary ring, and $R[x]$ the ring of polynomials in the indeterminate x with coefficients in R. If y is another arbitrary symbol or indeterminate, we may obviously construct the ring $R[x][y]$, whose elements are the polynomials in y, with coefficients from the ring $R[x]$. It will be clear that $R[x][y]$ coincides with the ring $R[y][x]$, and we shall henceforth denote this ring by $R[x, y]$, or by $R[y, x]$. Each element of $R[x, y]$, that is, each polynomial in the two

indeterminates x and y, is clearly expressible as a finite sum of polynomials of the special form

$$ax^iy^j,$$

where a is an element of R and i, j are nonnegative integers.

More generally, let $x_1, x_2, \cdots, x_n$ be indeterminates, and let us construct the following sequence of rings:

$$R_1 = R[x_1], R_2 = R_1[x_2], \cdots, R_n = R_{n-1}[x_n].$$

The ring R_n will be denoted henceforth by $R[x_1, x_2, \cdots, x_n]$ and, as in the case of two indeterminates, the order in which these indeterminates are written is immaterial. An element of $R[x_1, x_2, \cdots, x_n]$ may thus be considered as a polynomial in x_n with coefficients from $R[x_1, x_2, \cdots, x_{n-1}]$, or as a polynomial in x_1 with coefficients from $R[x_2, x_3, \cdots, x_n]$, and so on. The elements of $R[x_1, x_2, \cdots, x_n]$ may also be called polynomials in $x_1, x_2, \cdots, x_n$, with coefficients from R.

A polynomial of the special form

$$(14) \qquad ax_1^{i_1}x_2^{i_2} \cdots x_n^{i_n},$$

where a is an element of R and each exponent is a non-negative integer, may be called a *term*, with coefficient a. If $f = f(x_1, x_2, \cdots, x_n)$ is an element of $R[x_1, x_2, \cdots, x_n]$, then clearly f can be considered as a sum of terms,

$$(15) \qquad f = \sum a_{i_1i_2\ldots i_n}x_1^{i_1}x_2^{i_2} \cdots x_n^{i_n},$$

in which at most a finite number of terms have nonzero coefficients. Furthermore, we shall assume that in no two terms with nonzero coefficients are the exponents of all the indeterminates respectively equal, as otherwise these terms could be added to give a single term.

If $a \neq 0$, we define the degree of the term (14) to be $i_1 + i_2 + \cdots + i_n$. Then the *degree* of f, given by (15), is the degree of the term (or terms) of highest degree with nonzero coefficient. As in the case of polynomials in a single indeterminate, a nonzero element of R has degree 0, while the zero polynomial has no degree. The term of f in which each indeterminate has exponent 0 may conveniently be called the *constant term* of f.

It is sometimes convenient to consider the degree of a polynomial f in some one indeterminate. For example, if we consider f as a polynomial in x_1 with coefficients from the ring $R[x_2, x_3, \cdots, x_n]$, the degree of f as defined in §7 may be called the *degree of f in x_1*.

From the remarks of §7, it is clear that if R is an integral domain, then $R[x_1]$ is an integral domain. A repetition of the argument will show that $R[x_1, x_2, \cdots, x_n]$ is an integral domain if and only if R is an integral domain. If R is an integral domain, and f and g are any two nonzero elements of $R[x_1, x_2, \cdots, x_n]$, it follows that the degree of fg in x_1 is the sum of the degrees of f and of g in x_1. A similar statement obviously holds if x_1 is replaced by any one of the indeterminates. The reader may also verify that the degree of fg is the sum of the degrees of the factors.

There are a number of results of ordinary algebra, such as the expansion theorems for determinants, which actually take the form of identities in a number of variables. The remainder of this section will be devoted to proving a theorem which will be useful in extending such results to the case in which the elements are from a commutative ring.

We may emphasize that if f is an element of $R[x_1, x_2, \cdots, x_n]$, $f = 0$ means that f, when expressed in the form(15), has all coefficients $a_{i_1 i_2 \ldots i_n}$ equal to zero.

Now let I be the ring of integers, and thus $I[x_1, x_2, \cdots, x_n]$ is an integral domain. Let $g = g(x_1, x_2, \cdots, x_n)$ be an arbitrary element of $I[x_1, x_2, \cdots, x_n]$, and let us write g in the form

$$(16) \qquad g = \sum m_{i_1 i_2 \ldots i_n} x_1^{i_1} x_2^{i_2} \cdots x_n^{i_n},$$

as a sum of terms with integral coefficients. If now R is an arbitrary *commutative* ring with unit element e, and a_1, a_2, $\cdots$, a_n are elements of R, we define $g(a_1, a_2, \cdots, a_n)$ in a natural way as follows:

$$(17) \qquad g(a_1, a_2, \cdots, a_n) = \sum m_{i_1 i_2 \ldots i_n} e a_1^{i_1} a_2^{i_2} \cdots a_n^{i_n}.$$

Hence $g(a_1, a_2, \cdots, a_n)$ is a well-defined element of R. If $g(x_1, x_2, \cdots, x_n)$ has zero constant term, the e may be omitted in the right side of (17). Its presence is merely to take care of the fact that when we replace the x's by the corresponding a's we want the constant term $m = m_{00 \ldots 0}$ of $g(x_1, x_2, \cdots, x_n)$ to be replaced by me.

The case in which we are interested is that in which $g(x_1, x_2, \cdots, x_n) = 0$. This means that all integers $m_{i_1 i_2 \ldots i_n}$ in (16) are zero, and hence from (17) it follows that $g(a_1, a_2, \cdots, a_n) = 0$ for *all* choices of the elements a_1, a_2, $\cdots$, a_n from R.

THEOREM 11. *If $h(x_1, x_2, \cdots, x_n)$ and $k(x_1, x_2, \cdots, x_n)$ are elements of $I[x_1, x_2, \cdots, x_n]$ such that*

$$h(j_1, j_2, \cdots, j_n) = k(j_1, j_2, \cdots, j_n)$$

for every choice of $j_1, j_2, \cdots, j_n$ as positive integers, then

$$h(a_1, a_2, \cdots, a_n) = k(a_1, a_2, \cdots, a_n)$$

for every choice of $a_1, a_2, \cdots, a_n$ from any commutative ring R with unit element.

Let us set

$$g(x_1, x_2, \cdots, x_n) = h(x_1, x_2, \cdots, x_n) - k(x_1, x_2, \cdots, x_n).$$

In view of the remarks just made, we shall establish the

theorem by proving that $g(j_1, j_2, \cdots, j_n) = 0$ for every choice of $j_1, j_2, \cdots, j_n$ as positive integers implies that $g(x_1, x_2, \cdots, x_n) = 0$. This is a well-known result but we give a proof for the sake of completeness. First, if $n = 1$, we see from Theorem 8 that the equation $g(x_1) = 0$ can not have more roots in I than the degree of $g(x_1)$. Since we have assumed that $g(j_1) = 0$ for every positive integer j_1, it follows that $g(x_1)$ can have no degree, that is, that $g(x_1) = 0$, and this proves the statement for $n = 1$.

We now use the method of induction and prove our statement for arbitrary n on the assumption that it is true for $n - 1$. Clearly $g(x_1, x_2, \cdots, x_n)$ can not be of degree 0, hence if it is not zero it must have positive degree in some one of the indeterminates. Suppose, for concreteness, that it is of degree $k > 0$ in x_n. Thus we may write

$$(18) \quad g(x_1, x_2, \cdots, x_n) = g_k(x_1, x_2, \cdots, x_{n-1})x_n^k +$$

$$\cdots + g_0(x_1, x_2, \cdots, x_{n-1}),$$

with $g_k(x_1, x_2, \cdots, x_{n-1})$ a nonzero element of $I[x_1, x_2, \cdots, x_{n-1}]$. If $j_1, j_2, \cdots, j_{n-1}$ are arbitrary fixed positive integers, then $g(j_1, j_2, \cdots, j_{n-1}, x_n)$ is a polynomial in x_n with integral coefficients, and furthermore our hypothesis implies that $g(j_1, j_2, \cdots, j_{n-1}, j_n) = 0$ for every positive integer j_n. Hence, by the argument used above for the case of one indeterminate, $g(j_1, j_2, \cdots, j_{n-1}, x_n)$ must be the zero element of $I[x_n]$. This means that the coefficients of the different powers of x_n in (18) must vanish for $x_i = j_i$, $(i = 1, 2, \cdots, n - 1)$, where the j_i are arbitrary positive integers. In view of the induction hypothesis, this implies, in particular, that $g_k(x_1, x_2, \cdots, x_{n-1}) = 0$, which violates our assumption that $g(x_1, x_2, \cdots, x_n)$ is of degree k in x_n. Hence $g(x_1, x_2, \cdots, x_n) = 0$, and therefore $g(a_1, a_2, \cdots, a_n) = 0$ for every choice of the elements $a_1, a_2, \cdots, a_n$ from R. This completes the proof of the theorem.

In the statement of the theorem, we have restricted $j_1, j_2, \cdots, j_n$ to be positive integers. However, it will be clear that all that is required in the proof is that $g(j_1, j_2, \cdots, j_n) = 0$ for all choices of $j_1, j_2, \cdots, j_n$ from some infinite set of integers.

REFERENCES

Albert [1], Chapter II; [2], Chapter I; Birkhoff and MacLane [1], Chapter IV; Dubreil [1], Chapter VI (B); MacDuffee [2], Chapter V; [3], Chapter IV; van der Waerden [1], Chapters III, IV.

Divisors of zero in polynomial rings are discussed in Forsythe [1] and McCoy [4].

CHAPTER III

IDEALS AND HOMOMORPHISMS

11. Ideals. In accordance with previous use of the term, a *subring* of a ring R is a set S of elements of R such that, with respect to the addition and multiplication defined in R, S is itself a ring. Previously mentioned examples of subrings are the subring of all even integers in the ring of all integers, the subring of all integers in the field of rational numbers, and the subring of all finite subsets of $\mathcal{I}$ in the ring of all subsets of $\mathcal{I}$.

Although subrings are sometimes of interest, it will be shown presently that subsystems of more restricted type are of even more importance. These are the *ideals* which we proceed to define.

A set S of one or more elements of a ring R is called an *ideal* in R if and only if it has the following properties:

(i) If a and b are elements of S, then $a - b$ is an element of S.

(ii) If a is an element of S, then for every element r of R, ar and ra are elements of S.

We may first point out that an ideal S in R is necessarily a subring of R. By (i), if a is an element of S, then $0 = a - a$ is in S, and it then follows that $-a = 0 - a$ is also in S. Thus, if S contains any element, it also contains its negative and it therefore follows that if a and b are elements of S, $a + b = a - (-b)$ is in S. The sum of elements of S is an element of S, and clearly the product of elements of S is in S by (ii). All the defining properties of a ring, except the solvability of the equation $a + x = b$, are obviously satisfied for S since they are true for R, and this equation is solvable in S by (i). It follows that S is a ring and therefore a subring of R.

If R is a commutative ring, then always $ar = ra$, so that it is sufficient to require in condition (ii) that either of these products belongs to S. For noncommutative rings, an ideal according to our definition is often called a *two-sided ideal*.

We now mention a few examples to clarify these ideas. It is clear that the subring of even integers in the ring of all integers is, in fact, an ideal; for the product of an even integer by any integer, whether even or odd, is also even. On the other hand, the subring of integers in the ring of rational numbers is not an ideal since the product of an integer by a rational number is not necessarily an integer. The set of all finite subsets of $\mathcal{I}$ is an ideal in the ring of all subsets of $\mathcal{I}$, as can be verified by showing that properties (i) and (ii) are consequences of the definitions of addition and multiplication in this ring. Furthermore, the set A used in the proof of Theorem 9 on the existence of a g.c.d. of $f(x)$ and $g(x)$ is an ideal in the ring $F[x]$.

In any ring, there are two trivial ideals—the one consisting of the entire ring, and the other of the single element 0. This latter ideal is frequently called the *zero ideal* and any other ideal a *nonzero* ideal. It may be remarked that a division ring (in particular, a field) has *only* the two trivial ideals. For if S is a nonzero ideal in a division ring D, S contains an element $a \neq 0$, and therefore contains $aa^{-1} = e$. It then follows that S contains $xe = x$ for *every* element x of D, that is, that S is the entire ring D. As a matter of fact, this argument shows that in any ring R with unit element, an ideal containing an element having an inverse necessarily coincides with R. In particular, this is true if the ideal contains the unit element.

It will be convenient to have a special notation for ideals, and we shall frequently denote them by German letters, particularly by the letters $\mathfrak{a}$, $\mathfrak{b}$, $\mathfrak{c}$, $\mathfrak{f}$, $\mathfrak{m}$, $\mathfrak{n}$, $\mathfrak{p}$, $\mathfrak{q}$, $\mathfrak{r}$. If, however, an ideal consists of the entire ring R, we shall merely use the letter R to denote it. If $\mathfrak{a}$ and $\mathfrak{b}$ are ideals in the same ring R and if every element of $\mathfrak{a}$ is also an element of $\mathfrak{b}$, we may say that $\mathfrak{a}$ *is contained in* $\mathfrak{b}$ (or $\mathfrak{b}$ *contains* $\mathfrak{a}$) and indicate this fact in either of the following ways:

$$\mathfrak{a} \subseteq \mathfrak{b}, \qquad \mathfrak{b} \supseteq \mathfrak{a}.$$

If, in addition, $\mathfrak{a}$ is properly contained in $\mathfrak{b}$, that is, if $\mathfrak{b}$ contains at least one element which is not in $\mathfrak{a}$, and it is required to emphasize this fact, we write

$$\mathfrak{a} \subset \mathfrak{b} \quad \text{or} \quad \mathfrak{b} \supset \mathfrak{a}.$$

To indicate that a is an element of the ring R or of the ideal $\mathfrak{a}$, it will sometimes be convenient to use the notation, $a \varepsilon R$ or $a \varepsilon \mathfrak{a}$, respectively. If $\mathfrak{a} \subseteq \mathfrak{b}$ and $\mathfrak{b} \subseteq \mathfrak{a}$, then $\mathfrak{a}$ and $\mathfrak{b}$ contain precisely the same elements and we shall write $\mathfrak{a} = \mathfrak{b}$; otherwise $\mathfrak{a} \neq \mathfrak{b}$.

12. Ideals generated by a finite number of elements. Before proceeding to make further use of the concept of ideal, it will be well to give additional illustrations and to introduce some convenient notation. For the sake of simplicity, we consider only *commutative* rings throughout this section although the remarks can be suitably modified so as to apply to noncommutative rings as well.

Let R be a commutative ring, and a a nonzero element of R. If $\mathfrak{a}$ is *any* ideal which contains the element a, let us consider what other elements must necessarily be in $\mathfrak{a}$. Clearly $\mathfrak{a}$ must contain $a + a = 2a$; more generally, it must contain na, where n is any integer. Furthermore, by one of the defining properties of an ideal, $\mathfrak{a}$ must contain all elements of the form ra, $r \varepsilon R$. Also, then, $\mathfrak{a}$ contains all elements of the form

(19) $\qquad\qquad na + ra \qquad\qquad (n \ \varepsilon \ I, \ r \ \varepsilon \ R).$

If we denote by $\mathfrak{b}$ the set of *all* elements of the type (19), it may be shown that $\mathfrak{b}$ is itself an ideal in R. To show this, we note that if $n_1a + r_1a$ and $n_2a + r_2a$ are any elements of $\mathfrak{b}$, then

$$(n_1a + r_1a) - (n_2a + r_2a) = (n_1 - n_2)a + (r_1 - r_2)a$$

is also an element of $\mathfrak{b}$, so that the difference of two elements of $\mathfrak{b}$ is in $\mathfrak{b}$. If $n_1a + r_1a$ is any element of $\mathfrak{b}$, and r any element of R, then clearly

$$r(n_1a + r_1a) = 0a + (n_1r + rr_1)a$$

is in $\mathfrak{b}$, and the product of an element of $\mathfrak{b}$ by any element of R is therefore an element of $\mathfrak{b}$. Hence $\mathfrak{b}$ is an ideal, and clearly $\mathfrak{b} \subseteq \mathfrak{a}$. Since every ideal which contains the element a also contains the ideal $\mathfrak{b}$, $\mathfrak{b}$ is the "least" ideal which contains a, or, as we shall say, the ideal *generated by a*.

If R has a unit element e, the elements (19) of the ideal generated by a can be expressed in simpler form. In this case,

$$n_1a + r_1a = (n_1e + r_1)a,$$

where $n_1e + r_1$ is in R, so that the elements of $\mathfrak{b}$ are precisely those elements of the form

(20) $\qquad\qquad\qquad ra \qquad\qquad\qquad (r \ \varepsilon \ R).$

An ideal generated by an element a of R is called a *principal ideal* and usually denoted by the symbol (a). If R has a unit element, clearly $(e) = R$ or, more generally, if b is any element with an inverse, $(b) = R$. The zero ideal is obviously the principal ideal (0).

The reader may verify that the set of all elements of the form ra is an ideal even if R does not have a unit element. However, this ideal may not contain a itself and therefore is not the ideal generated by a. For example, if E is the ring of even integers, the principal ideal generated by the element 4 consists of all integers divisible by 4. However, in this case, the ideal of all elements of the form $4r$ consists of all integers divisible by 8. It is thus only for rings with unit element that the elements of the ideal (a) can necessarily be put in the simpler form ra, $r \ \varepsilon \ R$.

If m is a fixed integer in the ring I of all integers, the ideal (m) contains just the integers which are divisible by m. It is an interesting fact that the *only* ideals in I are principal ideals.

THEOREM 12. *In the ring I, every ideal is a principal ideal.*

Let $\mathfrak{a}$ be an ideal in I. If $\mathfrak{a}$ is the zero ideal, then $\mathfrak{a}$ is the principal ideal (0). Suppose, then, that $\mathfrak{a} \neq (0)$, and let m be the smallest positive integer in $\mathfrak{a}$. If n is any integer, then the familiar process of division leads to a relation of the form

$$n = qm + r,$$

where q and r are integers, and r is nonnegative and less than m. Now if n is an element of $\mathfrak{a}$, it follows that $n - qm$, being the difference of elements of $\mathfrak{a}$, is also in $\mathfrak{a}$. Hence $r \ \varepsilon \ \mathfrak{a}$ and, if r is greater than 0, this contradicts our assumption that m is the smallest positive integer in $\mathfrak{a}$. Therefore, $r = 0$, and $n = qm$, so that the elements of $\mathfrak{a}$ are all of the form qm. Since all elements of this form are necessarily in $\mathfrak{a}$, it follows that $\mathfrak{a} = (m)$, and the theorem is established. We may remark that since $(m) = (-m)$, $\mathfrak{a}$ can just as well be generated by $-m$.

A result similar to that of the preceding theorem holds for the ring of polynomials in one indeterminate with coefficients in a field.

THEOREM 13. *If F is a field and x an indeterminate, every ideal in $F[x]$ is a principal ideal.*

We omit the proof since it is almost identical with the proof of the preceding theorem with the exception that we choose $m(x)$ to be a polynomial of *least degree* in the given ideal, and make use of the division transformation for polynomials. The proof of Theorem 9 which established the existence of the g.c.d. of two polynomials in $F[x]$ made use of a similar argument.

In contrast with the situation which prevails in the rings I and $F[x]$, there are many rings in which not all ideals are principal. As a simple example, consider the ring $F[x, y]$ of polynomials in two indeterminates, with coefficients in the field F. This ring has a unit element and therefore the elements of a principal ideal can be put in the simple form (20). It is easy to verify that the set of all polynomials with zero constant terms is an ideal, which we may denote by c. Clearly c contains, along with other elements, the polynomials x and y; hence if c were a principal ideal $(f(x, y))$, we would have

$$(21) \qquad x = g(x, y)f(x, y), \quad y = h(x, y)f(x, y),$$

for suitable choice of $g(x, y)$ and $h(x, y)$ in $F[x, y]$. Since the polynomials of degree 0 have inverses, and any element with an inverse generates the entire ring, $f(x, y)$ can not be of degree 0. Since $c \neq (0)$, $f(x, y)$ can not be the zero polynomial and therefore must have positive degree. Furthermore, for the ring under consideration, the degree of a product of nonzero polynomials is the sum of the degrees of the factors. Hence the assumed relations (21) would show that $g(x, y)$ and $h(x, y)$ are of degree 0 while $f(x, y)$ is of the first degree. It is readily verified that (21) can not be satisfied for any such $f(x, y)$, and hence that c can not be a principal ideal.

This example leads to a consideration of ideals which are generated by a finite number of elements, in a sense to be presently defined. Let a_i $(i = 1, 2, \cdots, m)$ be a finite set of elements of the commutative ring R. By a natural extension of the argument used in defining the ideal generated by one element, it may be seen that any ideal which contains these elements must also contain all elements of the form

$$(22) \qquad \sum_{i=1}^{m} (n_i a_i + r_i a_i) \qquad (n_i \ \varepsilon \ I, \ r_i \ \varepsilon \ R).$$

Furthermore, the set of all elements of this form is an ideal $\mathfrak{b}$ which we shall call the ideal *generated by* the given elements a_i $(i = 1, 2, \cdots, m)$. The generating elements are said to form a *basis* of the ideal $\mathfrak{b}$, and we write

$$\mathfrak{b} = (a_1, a_2, \cdots, a_m).$$

This notation is consistent with that used for principal ideals, a principal ideal being an ideal with a basis consisting of just one element.

If R has a unit element, the argument by which we showed that all elements of the form (19) can be put in the form (20) proves that the elements (22) of $\mathfrak{b}$ can be expressed in the simpler form

$$(23) \qquad \sum_{i=1}^{m} r_i a_i \qquad (r_i \ \varepsilon \ R).$$

Let us again consider the ideal $\mathfrak{c}$ in $F[x, y]$ whose elements are the polynomials with zero constant terms. Since $\mathfrak{c}$ contains the element x, it contains $g(x, y)x$ for all $g(x, y)$ in $F[x, y]$; likewise it contains $h(x, y)y$ for all elements $h(x, y)$ in $F[x, y]$. Thus, finally, it contains all elements of the form

$$g(x, y)x + h(x, y)y,$$

and thus $\mathfrak{c} \supseteq (x, y)$. But any polynomial with zero constant term can be put in this form; hence $\mathfrak{c} \subseteq (x, y)$ and therefore $c = (x, y)$. Otherwise expressed, c has a basis consisting of the two elements x and y.

It may well happen that an ideal generated by two or more elements can also be generated by one element. This is certainly the case in the ring of integers, or in any other ring in which all ideals are principal. Thus, for example, consider the ideal $a = (6, 8)$ in I, the elements of which are of the form $6a + 8b$, where a and b are integers. Clearly a contains the element 2, as can be seen by taking $a = -1$, $b = 1$; hence all even integers are in a. Furthermore, from the form of the elements of a, it is obvious that all elements are even, and hence $(6, 8) = (2)$. More generally, let m, n be any two nonzero integers. By the proof of Theorem 12, the ideal $b = (m, n)$ is a principal ideal generated by the smallest positive integer d in the ideal b. Thus $(m, n) = (d)$, and from this it follows that there exist integers x, y, z, t such that

$$d = xm + yn, \quad m = zd, \quad n = td.$$

The last two of these equations show that d is a divisor of both m and n, while the first shows that any common divisor of m and n is a divisor of d. Thus d is a greatest common divisor (g.c.d.) of m and n, unique except for sign, and we have shown that the ideal generated by two integers is also generated by their g.c.d. This is also true for ideals generated by any finite number of integers.

Similar results hold for ideals in the ring $F[x]$, where F is a field. In fact, it is an immediate consequence of Theorem 9 on the existence of the g.c.d. of two polynomials that if $f(x)$ and $g(x)$ have $d(x)$ as their g.c.d., then

$$(f(x), g(x)) = (d(x)).$$

We have just pointed out some special results which hold in the rings I and $F[x]$ which share the property that every ideal is a principal ideal. If R is not a field, it is not generally true that every ideal in $R[x]$ is principal, and neither is there necessarily available a concept of greatest common divisor. However, if $f_i(x)$ $(i = 1, 2, \cdots, m)$ are elements of $R[x]$, it frequently happens that the ideal

$$(f_1(x), f_2(x), \cdots, f_m(x))$$

plays a role similar to that of the greatest common divisor of the $f_i(x)$, and in some applications is a natural generalization of this concept.

It may be of interest to point out that not every ideal in an arbitrary commutative ring necessarily has a basis consisting of a finite number of elements. As an illustration of an ideal without a finite basis, consider the ring B of all subsets of $\mathcal{I}$ as defined in §2, and let $\mathfrak{a}$ be the ideal which consists of all finite subsets of $\mathcal{I}$. Let us assume that

$$\mathfrak{a} = (a_1, a_2, \cdots, a_m),$$

and show that this leads to a contradiction. Since B has a unit element, the elements of $\mathfrak{a}$ will then be of the form

$$c = \sum_{i=1}^{m} a_i b_i,$$

where each $b_i \in B$. Now such an element c is a set of points of $\mathcal{I}$ which can contain no point not in some a_i, in view of the definitions of addition and multiplication in this ring. Thus no element of $\mathfrak{a}$ can contain a point of $\mathcal{I}$ other than those in some one of the a_i. However, since there are only a finite number of points in each a_i while $\mathcal{I}$ has an infinite number of points, it follows that there are some individual points of $\mathcal{I}$ which are not in any a_i. Hence there are some finite subsets of $\mathcal{I}$ which are not in any a_i, and thus the ideal $\mathfrak{a}$ can not have a finite basis.

In §45 we shall consider rings in which every ideal has

a finite basis and, in particular, shall determine a class of rings with this property.

13. Residue class rings. As an illustration of the ideas to be introduced presently, we return to a further study of the equivalence classes of the ring of integers with congruence modulo 6 as the equivalence relation under consideration. In accordance with the notation introduced in §6, let $\bar{n}$ denote the class of all integers equivalent to n, that is, differing from n by a multiple of 6. Thus the six different equivalence classes may be indicated by

$$\bar{0}, \bar{1}, \bar{2}, \bar{3}, \bar{4}, \bar{5},$$

the elements of the classes being the integers in the respective rows of the table exhibited in §6. Clearly $\bar{m} = \bar{n}$ (meaning that these classes consist of the same elements) if and only if $m \equiv n$ modulo 6. We may now define a new ring whose elements are these six equivalence classes. To do this, we need to give a definition of addition and multiplication of these classes which will satisfy all the defining properties of a ring. Let us first consider addition. It will be observed, for example, that the sum of any integer equivalent to 2 and any integer equivalent to 5 is always an integer equivalent to 7, and similarly for the sum of elements in other classes. We accordingly *define*

$$\bar{m} + \bar{n} = \overline{m + n}.$$

Likewise the product of classes may be *defined* as

$$\bar{m}\bar{n} = \overline{mn}.$$

It is not difficult to show that addition and multiplication are uniquely defined and that, with these definitions of addition and multiplication, the six equivalence classes are the elements of a ring. We shall not give a detailed proof of this fact since it is a special case of a result to be established below. This ring whose elements are the equivalence classes modulo 6 may be denoted by $I/(6)$, in accordance with a notation to be introduced presently. It is almost obvious that, except for the notation employed, the ring $I/(6)$ is precisely the ring I_6 of integers modulo 6, as defined in §2.

We now introduce a convenient notation which will henceforth be used constantly. Let R be an arbitrary ring, and $\mathfrak{n}$ an ideal in R. If $a - b \ \varepsilon \ \mathfrak{n}$, we may say that "$a$ is congruent to b modulo $\mathfrak{n}$," and write this in the abbreviated form

$$a \equiv b(\mathfrak{n}).$$

The notation $a \not\equiv b(\mathfrak{n})$ may then be conveniently used to indicate that a is not congruent to b modulo $\mathfrak{n}$, that is, that $a - b$ is not in $\mathfrak{n}$.

Since $a - 0 = a$ for every a, $a \equiv 0(\mathfrak{n})$ means merely that a is an element of $\mathfrak{n}$ and may thus be used interchangeably with the notation $a \ \varepsilon \ \mathfrak{n}$ introduced earlier. To indicate that a is not in $\mathfrak{n}$, we shall frequently write $a \not\equiv 0(\mathfrak{n})$.

The following are the most fundamental properties of congruence:

(i) *For every element a of R, $a \equiv a(\mathfrak{n})$;*

(ii) *If $a \equiv b(\mathfrak{n})$, then $b \equiv a(\mathfrak{n})$;*

(iii) *If $a \equiv b(\mathfrak{n})$ and $b \equiv c(\mathfrak{n})$, then $a \equiv c(\mathfrak{n})$;*

(iv) *If $a \equiv b(\mathfrak{n})$ and $c \equiv d(\mathfrak{n})$, then $a + c \equiv b + d(\mathfrak{n})$;*

(v) *If $a \equiv b(\mathfrak{n})$ and $c \equiv d(\mathfrak{n})$, then $ac \equiv bd(\mathfrak{n})$.*

The first two of these relations are almost obvious since every ideal contains the element 0, and the negative of any element of $\mathfrak{n}$ is an element of $\mathfrak{n}$. The proof of the third requires only that if $a - b \ \varepsilon \ \mathfrak{n}$ and $b - c \ \varepsilon \ \mathfrak{n}$, then

$$a - b + (b - c) = a - c \ \varepsilon \ \mathfrak{n}.$$

The relations (i), (ii), and (iii) show that congruence modulo $\mathfrak{n}$ is an equivalence relation in R as defined in §6. It will be noted that, according to the present notation, congruence modulo 6 in the ring of integers is merely congruence modulo the principal ideal (6).

To prove (iv) we note that $a - b \ \varepsilon \ \mathfrak{n}$ and $c - d \ \varepsilon \ \mathfrak{n}$ imply that

$$a - b + c - d = a + c - (b + d) \ \varepsilon \ \mathfrak{n}.$$

Finally, we prove relation (v) as follows. Since $a - b \ \varepsilon \ \mathfrak{n}$, we must have $(a - b)c \ \varepsilon \ \mathfrak{n}$; likewise $c - d \ \varepsilon \ \mathfrak{n}$ implies that $b(c - d) \ \varepsilon \ \mathfrak{n}$. Thus

$$(a - b)c + b(c - d) = ac - bd \ \varepsilon \ \mathfrak{n}.$$

It may be remarked that if $\mathfrak{n}$ were only a *subring* but not an ideal, the first four of the above relations would still be true and, in particular, we would still have an equivalence relation. However, property (v) is not generally true for subrings since it requires that the product of an element of $\mathfrak{n}$ by an element of R shall always be in $\mathfrak{n}$.

It is clear that, in a great many ways, congruence modulo $\mathfrak{n}$ behaves like the familiar equality of ordinary algebra, and the notation $a \equiv b(\mathfrak{n})$ is valuable because it suggests these similarities. However, it must not be assumed that *all* the familiar operations with equations can be carried over to congruences. For example, the congruence

$$xa \equiv xb(\mathfrak{n}),$$

does not, in general, imply that $a \equiv b(\mathfrak{n})$, even if $x \not\equiv 0(\mathfrak{n})$. As an illustration, note that in the ring of integers, we have $4 \cdot 4 \equiv 4 \cdot 1(6)$, but $4 \not\equiv 1(6)$.

It has already been pointed out that congruence modulo an ideal $\mathfrak{n}$ is a special instance of an equivalence relation. In fact, in the study of rings this kind of equivalence relation is of most frequent occurrence and of greatest interest. In accordance with a terminology frequently used in this connection, we may say that an equivalence class with reference to congruence modulo $\mathfrak{n}$ as the equivalence relation is a *residue class modulo* $\mathfrak{n}$ or, in case it is clear what ideal is referred to, simply a *residue class*.

If a is any element of R, let $\bar{a}$ denote the residue class which consists of all elements equivalent to a, that is, congruent to a modulo $\mathfrak{n}$. Otherwise expressed, the elements of the residue class $\bar{a}$ are precisely the elements of the form $a + n$, where $n \; \varepsilon \; \mathfrak{n}$. Thus $\bar{a}$ and $\bar{b}$ consist of the same elements if and only if $a \equiv b(\mathfrak{n})$, in which case we may write $\bar{a} = \bar{b}$. In view of relations (iv) and (v), it is clear that if a_1 is any element of $\bar{a}$, c_1 any element of $\bar{c}$, then $a_1 + c_1$ will always be in the class $\overline{a + c}$; and $a_1 c_1$ will be in the class $\overline{ac}$. This suggests natural definitions of addition and multiplication of these classes as follows:

$$\bar{a} + \bar{c} = \overline{a + c},$$

$$\bar{a}\bar{c} = \overline{ac}.$$

THEOREM 14. *The residue classes of a ring R, modulo an ideal* $\mathfrak{n}$, *with the above definitions of addition and multiplication of classes, form a ring—the* residue class ring *of R with respect to* $\mathfrak{n}$, *usually denoted by* $R/\mathfrak{n}$.

The proof of this theorem consists merely in verifying that the defining properties of a ring are satisfied. These are almost obvious in view of the definitions given above. For example, to prove the associative law of addition, we note that

$$\bar{a} + (\bar{b} + \bar{c}) = \bar{a} + \overline{(b + c)} = \overline{a + (b + c)},$$
$$(\bar{a} + \bar{b}) + \bar{c} = \overline{(a + b)} + \bar{c} = \overline{(a + b) + c},$$

and these are equal by the associative law of addition in R. The reader will have no difficulty in verifying the other properties, and the details are therefore omitted.

It is clear that the zero of the ring $R/\mathfrak{n}$ is $\bar{0}$, the set of elements of $\mathfrak{n}$ itself. However, we may sometimes write 0 in place of $\bar{0}$, since we have agreed to denote the zero of any ring by this familiar symbol. If R has a unit element e, then $R/\mathfrak{n}$ has the unit element $\bar{e}$, for $ae = ea = a$ implies that $\bar{a}\bar{e} = \bar{e}\bar{a} = \bar{a}$.

There are two ways of looking at the ring $R/\mathfrak{n}$, both of which are of some interest. On the one hand, as introduced above, the elements of the ring $R/\mathfrak{n}$ are the different residue classes of elements of R modulo $\mathfrak{n}$, and equality of elements $\bar{a}$ and $\bar{b}$ of $R/\mathfrak{n}$ means identity in the sense that $\bar{a}$ and $\bar{b}$ consist of the same elements of R. We have then to *define* addition and multiplication of elements of $R/\mathfrak{n}$. On the other hand, the elements of $R/\mathfrak{n}$ may be considered to be the same as the elements of R with the same definitions of addition and multiplication but with a new definition of "equality," namely, congruence modulo $\mathfrak{n}$. In this latter interpretation, two elements are not considered as "different" if they are congruent modulo $\mathfrak{n}$, that is, if they are in the same residue class modulo $\mathfrak{n}$. The first of these viewpoints will generally be used but the language can always be modified so as to apply equally to the second. We may remark that with the second of these viewpoints we might just as well not use *all* the elements of R but only a complete set of "different" elements, that is, one from each residue class. This was what was done in the definition of the ring of integers modulo n in §2, except that i' was written in place of i.

We shall now give another illustration of this important concept of residue class ring. Let F be the field of real numbers, and consider the ideal $\mathfrak{n} = (x^2 + 1)$ in the ring $F[x]$. If $f(x)$ is any element of $F[x]$, then by the division transformation (Theorem 5), we have

$$f(x) = q(x)(x^2 + 1) + a + bx,$$

where a and b are real numbers. Therefore every residue class modulo $\mathfrak{n}$ contains zero or a polynomial of at most the first degree. Furthermore, $a + bx$ and $c + dx$ are in different residue classes unless $a = c$ and $b = d$, for

$$a + bx \equiv c + dx (\mathfrak{n})$$

is impossible except in this case. Thus the different elements of $F[x]/\mathfrak{n}$ are precisely the residue classes

$$\overline{a + bx} = \bar{a} + \bar{b}\bar{x}.$$

From the definitions of addition and multiplication in $F[x]/\mathfrak{n}$, we see that

$$(\bar{a} + \bar{b}\bar{x}) + (\bar{c} + \bar{d}\bar{x}) = (\bar{a} + \bar{c}) + (\bar{b} + \bar{d})\bar{x},$$

and

$$(\bar{a} + \bar{b}\bar{x})(\bar{c} + \bar{d}\bar{x}) = (\bar{a}\bar{c} - \bar{b}\bar{d}) + (\bar{a}\bar{d} + \bar{b}\bar{c})\bar{x}.$$

The first of these is evident, and the second follows from the observation that

$$(a + bx)(c + dx) = ac - bd + (ad + bc)x + bd(x^2 + 1),$$

so that

$$(a + bx)(c + dx) \equiv (ac - bd) + (ad + bc)x \ (\mathfrak{n}).$$

The reader should note the similarity of these formulas with the ordinary rules for addition and multiplication of complex numbers—in fact, the ring $F[x]/(x^2 + 1)$ *is* the field of complex numbers except for the notation employed. Further reference to this example will be made in the next section.

An additional illustration may be of some interst. Let I be the ring of integers, and $\mathfrak{m}$ the ideal $(2, x^2 + x + 1)$ in the polynomial ring $I[x]$. By the argument used in the preceding example, with $x^2 + 1$ replaced by $x^2 + x + 1$, it can be seen that any residue class modulo $\mathfrak{m}$ contains an element of the form $a + bx$, where now a and b are integers. In this case, however, $\mathfrak{m}$ contains the integer 2 and therefore every integer is congruent modulo $\mathfrak{m}$ to either 0 or 1. Hence there are exactly four residue classes, namely,

$$\bar{0}, \quad \bar{1}, \quad \bar{x}, \quad \bar{x} + \bar{1}.$$

Furthermore, since

$$x(x + 1) = 1 + (x^2 + x + 1) - 2 \equiv 1(\mathfrak{m}),$$

we see that

$$\bar{x}(\bar{x} + \bar{1}) = \bar{1},$$

so that every nonzero element of $I[x]/\mathfrak{m}$ has an inverse and therefore $I[x]/\mathfrak{m}$ is a field. This is our first illustration of a finite field which is not of the form $I/(p)$, where p is a prime. As a matter of fact, it can be shown, although we omit the proof, that *any* finite field can be obtained as a residue class ring $I[x]/\mathfrak{m}$ for suitable choice of the ideal $\mathfrak{m}$.

14. **Homomorphisms and isomorphisms.** In this section we introduce some new concepts whose close connection with ideals will presently become apparent.

Let us first consider the ring I of integers and the ring $I/(6)$ of integers modulo 6. We have already pointed out that an arbitrary element n of I determines a unique element $\bar{n}$ of $I/(6)$, namely, the residue class to which n

belongs modulo 6. Obviously, many different integers n determine the same residue class. If we denote the correspondence of n to $\bar{n}$ by $n \to \bar{n}$, it is clear that if $n_1 \to \bar{n}_1$, $n_2 \to \bar{n}_2$, then

$$n_1 + n_2 \to \overline{n_1 + n_2} = \bar{n}_1 + \bar{n}_2,$$

and

$$n_1 n_2 \to \overline{n_1 n_2} = \bar{n}_1 \bar{n}_2.$$

Such a correspondence is an example of a *homomorphism* according to the definition which we shall now give.

Let R and S be two rings and let us assume that with each element a of R there is associated in some determined way a unique element a' of S such that always

$$(a + b)' = a' + b',$$

and

$$(ab)' = a'b'.$$

This correspondence, which may be denoted by $a \to a'$, is then called a *homomorphism of R into S*. The element a' may conveniently be called the *image* of a under this homomorphism, and clearly a single element a' of S may be the image of different elements of R.

We have not required that *every* element of S be the image of some element of R. If, however, this happens to be the case, we speak of a homomorphism of R *onto* S. This is also sometimes expressed by saying that R is *homomorphic* to S, or that S is a *homomorphic image* of R. At any rate, if we have a given homomorphism of R *into* S, the set S_1 of elements of S which are images of elements of R is easily seen to be a ring, and the homomorphism is actually a homomorphism of R *onto* the subring S_1 of S.

The familiar function notation is sometimes of convenience in the study of homomorphisms. Thus, it will be seen that a homomorphism h of R into S is actually a single-valued function $h(t)$ defined for all t in R, the values of the function being in S. Furthermore, this function has the following properties:

$$h(t_1 + t_2) = h(t_1) + h(t_2),$$

$$h(t_1 t_2) = h(t_1)h(t_2).$$

In this notation, $h(a)$ takes the place of the a' used above.

We now give further illustrations of homomorphisms. Let R be an arbitrary ring, and $R[x]$ the ring of polynomials in the indeterminate x, with coefficients in R. If $f(x)$ is any element of $R[x]$, the constant term of $f(x)$ may conveniently be denoted by $f(0)$. Then it is easy to verify that the correspondence

$$f(x) \rightarrow f(0)$$

defines a homomorphism of $R[x]$ onto R. Furthermore, if R is commutative, and a is any fixed element of R, the correspondence

$$f(x) \rightarrow f(a)$$

is a homomorphism of $R[x]$ onto R.

A most important example of a homomorphism is the homomorphism of R onto $R/\mathfrak{n}$ furnished by the correspondence $a \rightarrow \bar{a}$, where a is an element of R and $\bar{a}$ is the residue class to which a belongs modulo the ideal $\mathfrak{n}$. The fact that this is a homomorphism follows immediately from the definitions of addition and multiplication in $R/\mathfrak{n}$. It will be shown later (Theorem 17) that *every* homomorphism is essentially of this type.

Now let $a \rightarrow a'$ denote any homomorphism of the ring R into the ring S. Since, for every element a of R, $a + 0 = a$, it follows that $a' + 0' = a'$, and hence $0 \rightarrow 0'$, where $0'$

is the zero element of S. That is, in any homomorphism of R into S, the zero element of R must correspond to the zero element of S. Furthermore,

$$0 = a + (-a) \rightarrow a' + (-a)' = 0',$$

so that always $(-a)' = -a'$.

If R has a unit element e and we have a homomorphism of R onto S so that every element of S is the image of some element of R, then $ea = ae = a$ for every element a of R implies that $e'a' = a'e' = a'$ for every element a' of S. Hence e' is the unit element of S, and therefore a homomorphic image of a ring with unit element is necessarily a ring with unit element.

If in a homomorphism of R onto S, each element of S is the image of a unique element of R, so that the correspondence between elements of R and elements of S is unique in both directions, or, as it is usually called, a *one-to-one* correspondence, the homomorphism is said to be an *isomorphism*, and either ring is an *isomorphic image* of the other or *isomorphic to* the other. Since, in an isomorphism, the correspondence is one-to-one, it is sometimes denoted by $a \leftrightarrow a'$ rather than by $a \rightarrow a'$. If R is isomorphic to S, we shall denote this fact by writing $R \cong S$. It is easy to verify that isomorphism of rings is an equivalence relation, as defined in §6.

As an example of isomorphism, consider the one-to-one correspondence

$$p' \leftrightarrow \bar{p} \quad (p = 0, 1, \cdots, n - 1),$$

where p' and $\bar{p}$ are respectively elements of the ring I_n of integers modulo n, as defined in §2, and of the residue class ring $I/(n)$. This is evidently an isomorphism since if $p' \leftrightarrow \bar{p}$, $q' \leftrightarrow \bar{q}$, it follows that

$$p' + q' \leftrightarrow \bar{p} + \bar{q} \text{ and } p'q' \leftrightarrow \bar{p}\bar{q}.$$

Thus $I_n \cong I/(n)$, a fact which was essentially pointed out in §13 where it was observed (for the case in which $n = 6$) that the rings are identical except for the notation employed.

As a further example, let us return to the ring $F[x]/(x^2 + 1)$, where F is the field of real numbers, which was introduced in the preceding section. Let i be a square root of -1, and consider the correspondence

$$\bar{a} + \bar{b}\bar{x} \rightarrow a + bi,$$

where $\bar{a} + \bar{b}\bar{x}$ is an element of $F[x]/(x^2 + 1)$, and $a + bi$ is the corresponding complex number. It is clear that this is a one-to-one correspondence between the elements of $F[x]/(x^2 + 1)$ and the elements of the field of all complex numbers. Furthermore, it is an isomorphism since the rules for addition and multiplication of elements of $F[x]/(x^2 + 1)$ are precisely the rules for combining the corresponding complex numbers. This isomorphism should not be surprising in view of the fact that in $F[x]/(x^2 + 1)$, we have

$$\bar{x}^2 + \bar{1} = \bar{0},$$

and thus $\bar{x}$ takes the place of the complex number i. In this example, we have assumed that the reader is already familiar with complex numbers but, as a matter of fact, the field of complex numbers may well be *defined* as $F[x]/(x^2 + 1)$, where F is the field of real numbers.

Suppose now that R and S are any two isomorphic rings. If $ab = ba$ in R it follows that $a'b' = b'a'$ in S, and conversely, so that an isomorphic image of a commutative ring is a commutative ring. It is also easy to verify that *an isomorphic image of a field or division ring is respectively a field or division ring*. Similarly, R has proper divisors of zero if and only if S has proper divisors of zero; hence *an isomorphic image of an integral domain is an integral domain*.

Inasmuch as all properties of addition and multiplication are preserved under isomorphism, isomorphic rings are sometimes said to be *abstractly identical* and, for most purposes, it is not necessary to distinguish between them. However, it must be kept in mind that isomorphic rings may have separate existence. For example, it is possible for a ring to be isomorphic to a proper subring of itself. As an illustration of this, consider the ring $R[x]$, where R is an arbitrary ring and x an indeterminate. It is easy to verify that the set of elements of $R[x]$ in which x occurs to even powers only, that is, the polynomials in x^2, is a proper subring of $R[x]$ which we may denote by $R[x^2]$. Then the correspondence

$$a_0 + a_1x + \cdots + a_nx^n \leftrightarrow a_0 + a_1x^2 + \cdots + a_nx^{2n}$$

is a one-to-one correspondence between the elements of $R[x]$ and those of $R[x^2]$. Furthermore, under this correspondence, the sum (product) of two elements corresponds to the sum (product) of the corresponding elements, and hence this is an isomorphism.

Before showing the relation of homomorphisms to ideals, we first prove two simple theorems on isomorphisms.

THEOREM 15. *Every field with p elements (p a prime) is isomorphic to $I/(p)$.*

It was pointed out above that $I_p \cong I/(p)$, and Theorem 2 shows that I_p is a field. Hence $I/(p)$ is a field with the p elements

$$\bar{n} \qquad (n = 0, 1, \cdots, p - 1).$$

Now let F be any field with p elements, and denote the unit element of F by e. Then, by Theorem 3, it follows that the number of elements of F is a power of the characteristic, and hence the characteristic of F must be the prime p. The p elements

$$ne \qquad (n = 0, 1, \cdots, p - 1)$$

are therefore distinct and are all the elements of F. The correspondence $ne \leftrightarrow \bar{n}$ is thus a one-to-one correspondence between elements of F and those of $I/(p)$. If $n_1 e$ and $n_2 e$ are two elements of F, and

$$n_1 + n_2 = qp + r,$$

where $0 \leq r < p$, we see that

$$n_1 e + n_2 e = qpe + re = re.$$

However, we also have $\bar{n}_1 + \bar{n}_2 = \bar{r}$, and thus

$$n_1 e + n_2 e \leftrightarrow \bar{n}_1 + \bar{n}_2 .$$

Similarly, it may be seen that

$$(n_1 e)(n_2 e) \leftrightarrow \bar{n}_1 \bar{n}_2,$$

and therefore the correspondence is an isomorphism.

THEOREM 16. *A field F of characteristic p, all of whose elements satisfy the equation*

$$x^p - x = 0$$

is isomorphic to $I/(p)$. Furthermore, in the ring of polynomials in x with coefficients in $I/(p)$, we have

$$x^p - x = x(x - \bar{1})(x - \bar{2}) \cdots (x - \overline{p - 1}).$$

By Theorem 8, F can not have more than p elements, and thus is a finite field. By Theorem 3, the number of elements is a positive power of the characteristic p, hence is exactly p. The preceding theorem then shows that

$F \cong I/(p)$. The last part of the theorem follows from Theorem 7 in view of the fact that all elements of $I/(p)$ do satisfy the equation $x^p - x = 0$, as shown in §5 for the field I_p which is isomorphic to $I/(p)$.

We now return to the study of homomorphisms. Let h be a given homomorphism $a \to a'$ of R onto S, and denote by $\mathfrak{k}$ the set of all elements of R which correspond to the zero element $0'$ of S. We shall first show that $\mathfrak{k}$ is an ideal in R. If a and b are elements of $\mathfrak{k}$, then $a' = b' = 0'$, hence

$$(a - b)' = a' - b' = 0',$$

so that $a - b$ is also in $\mathfrak{k}$. Furthermore, if a is in $\mathfrak{k}$, and r is any element of R, we have

$$(ar)' = a'r' = 0' \cdot r' = 0',$$

and

$$(ra)' = r'a' = r' \cdot 0' = 0'.$$

Thus the defining properties of an ideal are satisfied, and $\mathfrak{k}$ is an ideal. It is sometimes convenient to call the ideal $\mathfrak{k}$ the *kernel* of the homomorphism h of R onto S.

We shall now prove the following fundamental theorem on homomorphisms:

THEOREM 17. *If $\mathfrak{n}$ is an ideal in R, there exists a homomorphism of R onto $R/\mathfrak{n}$, with kernel $\mathfrak{n}$. Furthermore, if h is a homomorphism of R onto a ring S, then S is isomorphic to $R/\mathfrak{k}$, where $\mathfrak{k}$ is the kernel of the homomorphism h.*

The truth of the first statement was pointed out shortly after homomorphisms were first defined at the beginning of this section. To prove the second part, let h be a homomorphism of R onto S, with kernel $\mathfrak{k}$. As above, we may denote the correspondence h by $a \to a'$. Let $\bar{a}$ denote the residue class to which a belongs modulo $\mathfrak{k}$, that is, the elements of $\bar{a}$ are of the form $a + k$, $k \,\varepsilon\, \mathfrak{k}$. Since

$$(a + k)' = a' + k' = a' + 0' = a',$$

it is seen that all elements of a residue class $\bar{a}$ correspond to the same element a' of S. On the other hand, no element of R not in $\bar{a}$ can correspond to a', for if $b' = a'$, it follows that

$$(a - b)' = a' - a' = 0',$$

and $a - b \; \varepsilon \; \mathfrak{k}$; thus a and b are in the same residue class modulo $\mathfrak{k}$.

These remarks show that the correspondence $\bar{a} \to a'$ is a one-to-one correspondence between the elements of $R/\mathfrak{k}$ and the elements of S. Let $\bar{a}$ and $\bar{b}$ be arbitrary elements of $R/\mathfrak{k}$, and a and b arbitrary elements of R in these respective residue classes. Then, since the correspondence $a \to \bar{a}$ has already been shown to define a homomorphism of R onto $R/\mathfrak{k}$, and the correspondence $a \to a'$ is given as a homomorphism of R onto S, it follows that the correspondence $\bar{a} \to a'$ has the following properties:

$$\bar{a} + \bar{b} = \overline{a + b} \to (a + b)' = a' + b',$$

$$\bar{a}\bar{b} = \overline{ab} \to (ab)' = a'b'.$$

These, however, are merely the properties which show that the correspondence $\bar{a} \to a'$ is a homomorphism of $R/\mathfrak{k}$ onto S and, since it is a one-to-one correspondence, it is an isomorphism. This completes the proof of the theorem.

We have now established the close connection between ideals and homomorphisms which was mentioned earlier. For a homomorphism of R onto a ring S determines a unique ideal $\mathfrak{k}$ in R, namely, the kernel of the homomorphism. Conversely, any ideal $\mathfrak{k}$ in R determines a homomorphism of R onto the ring $R/\mathfrak{k}$, and the kernel of this homomorphism is precisely $\mathfrak{k}$.

Since R is itself an ideal in R, it is clear that every ring is homomorphic to a ring consisting of the zero element alone (as is evident anyway by direct observation), namely, the residue class ring R/R. We may also remark that always $R/(0) \cong R$ and, since the only ideals in a division ring D are the trivial ideals (0) and D, it follows that the *only* homomorphic image of a division ring is actually an isomorphic image—unless it consists of the zero alone.

If R is homomorphic to S and $\mathfrak{a}$ is an ideal in R, then it is easily verified that the set of all elements of S which are images of elements of $\mathfrak{a}$ is an ideal in S which we may naturally call the *image* of $\mathfrak{a}$ under the given homomorphism. Conversely, if we start with an ideal $\mathfrak{b}$ in S, the set of *all* elements of R whose images are in $\mathfrak{b}$ is an ideal in R—the *inverse image* of $\mathfrak{b}$. According to this terminology, the kernel of the given homomorphism is just the inverse image of the zero ideal. If $\mathfrak{b}$ is the image of $\mathfrak{a}$, then clearly $\mathfrak{a}$ is contained in the inverse image of $\mathfrak{b}$. As an illustration of these concepts, consider the homomorphism $n \rightarrow \bar{n}$ of I onto $I/(6)$. Under this homomorphism, the image of the ideal (9) in I is the ideal $(\bar{3})$ in $I/(6)$. Furthermore, the inverse image of $(\bar{3})$ is the ideal (3) in I, and clearly $(9) \subset (3)$.

We shall now prove

THEOREM 18. *If $\mathfrak{n}$ is an ideal in R, and R_1 is a subring of R having only the zero in common with $\mathfrak{n}$, then $R/\mathfrak{n}$ contains a subring isomorphic to R_1.*

The correspondence $a \rightarrow \bar{a}$, where a is an element of R_1 and $\bar{a}$ the residue class to which a belongs modulo $\mathfrak{n}$, is clearly a homomorphism of R_1 into $R/\mathfrak{n}$. If a and b are elements of R_1 with the same image element, then, by the fundamental theorem on homomorphisms, $a - b \ \varepsilon \ \mathfrak{n}$. From this, it follows that $a = b$ since the only element of R_1 in $\mathfrak{n}$ is the zero. The correspondence thus defines an isomorphism of R_1 onto a subring of $R/\mathfrak{n}$, that is, $R/\mathfrak{n}$ contains a subring isomorphic to R_1 .

As an almost trivial application of this theorem, consider again the field $F[x]/(x^2 + 1)$, where F is the field of real numbers. Since the principal ideal $(x^2 + 1)$ contains no nonzero real number, the theorem asserts that $F[x]/(x^2 + 1)$ contains a subfield isomorphic to the field F.

15. **Additional remarks on ideals.** There are several methods by which new ideals may be constructed from given ideals, and we shall now mention two of these.

If $\mathfrak{a}$ and $\mathfrak{b}$ are ideals in a ring R, let us denote by $\mathfrak{a} \cap \mathfrak{b}$ the *intersection* of $\mathfrak{a}$ and $\mathfrak{b}$, that is, the set of elements of R belonging to both $\mathfrak{a}$ and $\mathfrak{b}$. It is readily verified that $\mathfrak{a} \cap \mathfrak{b}$ satisfies the defining properties of an ideal and hence is an ideal in R. In fact, the intersection of any finite or infinite set of ideals in R is an ideal in R. The intersection of a finite number of ideals $\mathfrak{a}_i$ $(i = 1, 2, \cdots, n)$ in R is sometimes denoted by

$$\mathfrak{a}_1 \cap \mathfrak{a}_2 \cap \cdots \cap \mathfrak{a}_n .$$

The principal ideal (a), as defined in §12, is actually the intersection of all ideals in R which contain the element a. For it was shown that any ideal which contains a contains the ideal (a), and clearly a is an element of (a). Likewise, the ideal generated by a finite number of elements is just the intersection of all ideals which contain these elements.

Again, let $\mathfrak{a}$ and $\mathfrak{b}$ be ideals in the ring R. It is easy to see that the *union* of these ideals, that is, the set of elements in $\mathfrak{a}$ or in $\mathfrak{b}$ (or in both), is not necessarily an ideal. For example, the union of the ideals (4) and (6) in the ring I consists of the integers divisible by 4 or by 6. If this union were an ideal it would have to contain $6 - 4$ since it contains 6 and 4, but obviously 2 is divisible by neither 4 nor 6.

Let us consider, however, the set of all elements of R of the form

$$a + b \qquad\qquad (a \ \varepsilon \ \mathfrak{a}, \ b \ \varepsilon \ \mathfrak{b}).$$

Since every ideal contains the zero of R, it is clear that this set contains all elements of $\mathfrak{a}$ and all elements of $\mathfrak{b}$. Furthermore, it is readily verified that this set is an ideal in R which we call the *sum* of the ideals $\mathfrak{a}$ and $\mathfrak{b}$, and denote by $(\mathfrak{a}, \mathfrak{b})$. Now any ideal in R which contains both $\mathfrak{a}$ and $\mathfrak{b}$ clearly contains the ideal $(\mathfrak{a}, \mathfrak{b})$, and since $(\mathfrak{a}, \mathfrak{b})$ contains both $\mathfrak{a}$ and $\mathfrak{b}$ it follows that the sum of $\mathfrak{a}$ and $\mathfrak{b}$ is just the intersection of all ideals which contain both $\mathfrak{a}$ and $\mathfrak{b}$.

The sum of the ideals (4) and (6) in I contains $6 - 4 = 2$, and hence contains all even integers. It is obvious that all elements of the sum are even and hence that the sum is just the ideal (2). In general, the sum of two ideals (m) and (n) in I is just the principal ideal generated by the g.c.d. of m and n. The intersection of the ideals (m) and (n) is the principal ideal generated by the least common multiple of m and n.

The *sum* of a finite number of ideals $\mathfrak{a}_i$ $(i = 1, 2, \cdots, m)$ consists of all elements of R expressible in the form

$$a_1 + a_2 + \cdots + a_m \quad (a_i \ \varepsilon \ \mathfrak{a}_i, i = 1, 2, \cdots, m),$$

and is usually denoted by the symbol

$$(\mathfrak{a}_1, \quad \mathfrak{a}_2, \quad \cdots, \quad \mathfrak{a}_m).$$

In this language, it is seen that if a_i $(i = 1, 2, \cdots, m)$ is a basis of an ideal in the commutative ring R, then this ideal is just the sum of the principal ideals (a_i), $i = 1, 2, \cdots, m$. However, in this case, instead of writing

$$((a_1), \ (a_2), \ \cdots, \ (a_m)),$$

we use the simpler notation

$$(a_1, a_2, \cdots, a_m)$$

introduced in §12.

In like manner, if $\mathfrak{m}$ is an ideal in the commutative ring R, and a an element of R, we usually write $(\mathfrak{m}, a)$ in place of the more cumbersome notation $(\mathfrak{m},(a))$. In view of our remarks above, it follows that $(\mathfrak{m}, a)$ is the "least" ideal containing a together with all elements of $\mathfrak{m}$. The elements of $(\mathfrak{m}, a)$ are of the form

$$b + na + ra \qquad (b \ \varepsilon \ \mathfrak{m}, \ n \ \varepsilon \ I, \ r \ \varepsilon \ R).$$

By the remarks of §12, if R has a unit element these elements are expressible in the simpler form

$$b + ra \qquad\qquad (b \ \varepsilon \ \mathfrak{m}, \ r \ \varepsilon \ R).$$

16. **Conditions that a residue class ring be a field.** We again restrict R to be a *commutative* ring. If $\mathfrak{m}$ is an ideal in R it may happen that $R/\mathfrak{m}$ is a field. For example, we have already pointed out that if F is the field of real numbers, $F[x]/(x^2 + 1)$ is a field, isomorphic to the field of complex numbers. Also, $I/(p)$ is a field for each prime p. Another example is $I[x]/(2, x^2 + x + 1)$, which was shown to be a field of four elements. We shall now seek general conditions on the ideal $\mathfrak{m}$ which will assure us that $R/\mathfrak{m}$ is a field.

Let us start with an ideal $\mathfrak{m}$ in R for which $R/\mathfrak{m}$ is assumed to be a field, and see what information this gives about the ideal $\mathfrak{m}$. As usual, we denote the residue class to which a belongs modulo $\mathfrak{m}$ by $\bar{a}$. By the definition of a field, $R/\mathfrak{m}$ contains more than one element and hence $\mathfrak{m} \subset R$; also if $\bar{a} \neq 0$, and $\bar{b}$ is any element of $R/\mathfrak{m}$, there is an $\bar{x}$ in $R/\mathfrak{m}$ such that $\bar{a}\bar{x} = \bar{b}$. In other words, if a is an element not in $\mathfrak{m}$, and b any element of R, there is an element x of R such that $ax \equiv b(\mathfrak{m})$, that is, $b = ax + m_1$, where $m_1 \; \varepsilon \; \mathfrak{m}$. This implies that any ideal which contains $\mathfrak{m}$ and also contains a must contain b. But since b is *any* element of R, it follows that the only ideal which contains $\mathfrak{m}$ and the element a is the entire ring R. Thus, in the notation of the preceding section, this means that $(\mathfrak{m}, a) = R$. Since this is true for every element a not in $\mathfrak{m}$, it follows that $\mathfrak{m}$ can not be properly contained in any other ideal except R. For if $\mathfrak{m} \subset \mathfrak{n}$, and c is an element of $\mathfrak{n}$ not in $\mathfrak{m}$, then $(\mathfrak{m}, c) \subseteq \mathfrak{n}$. But $(\mathfrak{m}, c) = R$ and hence $\mathfrak{n} = R$.

We now make the following general definition. An ideal $\mathfrak{m} \neq R$ which is not properly contained in any ideal except R itself may be called a *maximal ideal in R*. Otherwise expressed, $\mathfrak{m}$ is a maximal ideal in R if $\mathfrak{m} \subset R$ and has the property that if $\mathfrak{n}$ is an ideal such that $\mathfrak{m} \subset \mathfrak{n} \subseteq R$, then $\mathfrak{n} = R$.

We have therefore shown that if $R/\mathfrak{m}$ is a field, $\mathfrak{m}$ must be a maximal ideal in R. It is natural to inquire whether the converse of this is also true, but a simple example will show that it is not. Consider the ideal (4) in the ring E of even integers. It is easy to see that (4) is maximal in E for if n is an even integer not divisible by 4, the greatest common divisor of 4 and n is 2, so that $(4, n) = (2) = E$. However, $E/(4)$ is not a field since $2^2 \equiv 0(4)$, while $2 \not\equiv 0(4)$, and in a field the square of a nonzero element can not be zero. It is interesting to note that (6) is also a maximal ideal in E but in this case there is no even integer m such that $m^2 \equiv 0(6)$, $m \not\equiv 0(6)$. Furthermore, it is easily verified that $E/(6)$ *is* a field, in fact, it is isomorphic to $I/(3)$. These remarks serve to illustrate and partly to suggest the following general result:

THEOREM 19. *If $\mathfrak{m}$ is an ideal in the commutative ring R,*

$R/\mathfrak{m}$ *is a field if and only if both the following conditions are satisfied:*

(i) $\mathfrak{m}$ *is a maximal ideal in* R,

(ii) *If* $x^2 \equiv 0(\mathfrak{m})$, *then* $x \equiv 0(\mathfrak{m})$.

If $R/\mathfrak{m}$ is a field, we have already shown that $\mathfrak{m}$ is a maximal ideal, and it is clear that the second condition is also satisfied since a field has no proper divisors of zero.

Let us now assume the conditions (i) and (ii), and prove that $R/\mathfrak{m}$ is a field. Let a be any fixed element of R not in $\mathfrak{m}$, and b any element of R. Our proof will be completed by showing that there is an element x of R such that $ax \equiv b(\mathfrak{m})$, and thus in $R/\mathfrak{m}$, $\bar{a}\bar{x} = \bar{b}$.

Since a is not in $\mathfrak{m}$, condition (ii) assures us that a^2 is not in $\mathfrak{m}$, and hence not all elements of the form ax, $x \, \varepsilon \, R$, are in $\mathfrak{m}$. But the set of elements of this form is an ideal $\mathfrak{n}$ and because of the maximality of $\mathfrak{m}$, we see that $(\mathfrak{m}, \mathfrak{n}) = R$. That is, every element of R is expressible in the form $m + ax$ for suitable choice of m in $\mathfrak{m}$, x in R. In particular, b is so expressible, which merely states that there is an element x of R such that $ax \equiv b(\mathfrak{m})$, and the theorem is proved.

COROLLARY. *If* R *is commutative and has a unit element,* $R/\mathfrak{m}$ *is a field if and only if* $\mathfrak{m}$ *is a maximal ideal in* R.

To establish this, we only need to show that if R has a unit element, condition (ii) is a consequence of condition (i). Let $\mathfrak{m}$ be maximal in R and suppose that $d \not\equiv 0(\mathfrak{m})$. Then $(\mathfrak{m}, d) = R$ and, since R has a unit element, each element of $(\mathfrak{m}, d)$ is expressible in the form

$$m + rd \qquad (m \, \varepsilon \, \mathfrak{m}, r \, \varepsilon \, R).$$

Hence, in particular, the unit element 1 is so expressible, that is,

$$1 = m_1 + r_1 d$$

for suitable choice of m_1 in $\mathfrak{m}$, r_1 in R. Multiplication of this equation by d shows that

$$d = m_1 d + r_1 d^2,$$

from which it follows that $d^2 \not\equiv 0(\mathfrak{m})$, for otherwise we would have $d \equiv 0(\mathfrak{m})$, contrary to hypothesis.

It was shown in Theorem 2 that I_n is a field if and only if n is a prime. Since $I_n \cong I/(n)$, the result just established shows that an ideal (n) in I is a maximal ideal if and only if n is a prime. This is easily verified directly since it is equivalent to the statement that the g.c.d. of n and an integer not divisible by n is necessarily 1 if and only if n is a prime.

Another illustration is the following. Let $F[x]$ be the ring of polynomials in the indeterminate x, with coefficients in the *field F*. If $p(x)$ is an *irreducible* element, and $g(x)$ any element of $F[x]$ not divisible by $p(x)$, the results of §9 show that the g.c.d. of $p(x)$ and $g(x)$ is 1, and hence that

$$(p(x), g(x)) = (1) = F[x].$$

This shows that the ideal $(p(x))$ is a maximal ideal in $F[x]$, and it follows that the residue class ring $F[x]/(p(x))$ is necessarily a field. A special case, already mentioned on several occasions, is the field $F[x]/(x^2 + 1)$, where F is the field of real numbers.

REFERENCES

Birkhoff and MacLane [1], Chapters I, XIII; Bourbaki [1], §8; Dubreil [1], Chapter IV(D); MacDuffee [2], Chapter V; van der Waerden [1], Chapter III.

An alternative formulation of Theorem 19 will be found in Stone [2], §18.

SOME IMBEDDING THEOREMS

17. A fundamental theorem. If R is a given ring, we may sometimes be interested in constructing a ring S which contains R as a subring and which has some property not present in R. In this chapter, we shall consider some constructions of this type. However, before proceeding, we shall prove a fundamental theorem which states that it is often sufficient to construct a ring containing a subring *isomorphic* to R.

First we prove the following almost obvious

LEMMA. *If S is a ring, and T a set of elements in one-to-one correspondence with the elements of S, then addition and multiplication may be defined in T in such a way that T is a ring isomorphic to S.*

Let us denote the given one-to-one correspondence by $a \leftrightarrow a'$, where a is an element of S and a' the corresponding element of T. To complete the proof it is only necessary to define addition and multiplication in T in the following natural way:

$$a' + b' = (a + b)',$$
$$a'b' = (ab)',$$

and to observe that T is then a ring isomorphic to S.

THEOREM 20. *If R and S are rings with no elements in common, and S contains a subring S_1 isomorphic to R, then there exists a ring T which is isomorphic to S and which contains R as a subring.*

Let T be the set whose elements are the elements of R together with the elements of S not in S_1. The elements of

S may be put in a one-to-one correspondence $a \leftrightarrow a'$ with the elements of T in the following way. Let a be an element of S. If a is in S_1, we let a' be the element of R to which a corresponds by the given isomorphism $R \cong S_1$. If a is not in S_1, we let $a' = a$. By the lemma, it then follows that one may define addition and multiplication in T in such a way that T is a ring isomorphic to S. Furthermore, the definitions are such that, as elements of the ring T, elements of R combine precisely as in the ring R, and hence T contains R as a subring.

For many purposes, it is not necessary to distinguish between isomorphic rings. Hence this theorem assures us that if R and S satisfy the stated hypotheses, there is no loss of generality, in so far as properties preserved by isomorphism are concerned, in assuming that S *contains* R, since S can be replaced by the isomorphic ring T with this property. We shall now give some illustrations of the use of this principle.

As originally defined in §7, the ring $R[x]$ of polynomials in an indeterminate x with coefficients from the arbitrary ring R has "constant" elements of the form ax^0, $a \, \varepsilon \, R$. It may now be verified that by the correspondence

$$a \leftrightarrow ax^0,$$

R is isomorphic to a subring of $R[x]$, and the observation that we can simply write a in place of ax^0 is a special application of the principle just enunciated. For, by so doing, we are identifying R with this subring, and hence assuming that $R[x]$ actually contains R.

As a further illustration, let R, for the moment, be the field of real numbers and S the ring of real matrices of order 2 as defined in §2. Let S_1 be the set of all elements of S of the form

$$\begin{bmatrix} a & 0 \\ 0 & a \end{bmatrix},$$

where a is a real number. It is easy to see that S_1 is a subring of S and that R is isomorphic to S_1 by the correspondence

$$a \leftrightarrow \begin{bmatrix} a & 0 \\ 0 & a \end{bmatrix}.$$

Thus, in a study of the ring S, it is frequently convenient to replace S_1 by R, that is, to write a in place of the matrix

$$\begin{bmatrix} a & 0 \\ 0 & a \end{bmatrix}.$$

We shall give one further illustration in connection with Theorem 18 which states that if $\mathfrak{n}$ is an ideal in the ring R, and R_1 is a subring of R having only the zero in common with $\mathfrak{n}$, then $R/\mathfrak{n}$ contains a subring isomorphic to R_1. In this case, it is often convenient to identify R_1 with the isomorphic subring of $R/\mathfrak{n}$, and hence to consider that $R/\mathfrak{n}$ *contains* R_1 as a subring. One important application of this will now be presented in some detail.

Let F be a field, and $F[x]$ the ring of polynomials in the indeterminate x, with coefficients in F. Now let $f(x)$ be an element of $F[x]$ of positive degree, and

$$f(x) = ap_1(x)p_2(x) \cdots p_r(x)$$

the unique factorization of $f(x)$ into irreducible monic factors, distinct or identical, according to Theorem 10. Consider a single irreducible factor $p_1(x)$ of $f(x)$, and let us assume that $p_1(x)$ has degree > 1. It was pointed out at the end of §16 that $F[x]/(p_1(x))$ is a field, which we may conveniently denote by F_1. Since the principal ideal $(p_1(x))$ contains no nonzero element of F, it follows by the above remarks that F_1 contains a subfield isomorphic to F, which we proceed to identify with F. According to the usual notation, if

$$g(x) = b_m x^m + b_{m-1} x^{m-1} + \cdots + b_0$$

is an element of $F[x]$, let $\overline{g(x)}$ denote the corresponding element of F_1. Since the coefficients b_i are in F, it follows that $\bar{b}_i = b_i$ inasmuch as we have identified elements of F with the corresponding elements of F_1. Hence we see that

$$\overline{g(x)} = g(\bar{x}).$$

In particular, since elements of $(p_1(x))$ correspond to the zero element of F_1, it follows that $p_1(\bar{x}) = 0$. Now if y is a new indeterminate, it is clear that $f(y)$ and the $p_i(y)$ are elements of $F_1[y]$ since F_1 contains F. However, in $F_1[y]$, $p_1(y)$ is no longer irreducible since $p_1(\bar{x}) = 0$ implies that $p_1(y)$ has $y - \bar{x}$ as a factor by the Factor Theorem. We have thus shown that if $f(y)$ is factored into irreducible factors in $F_1[y]$, it contains at least one more factor of the first degree than when factored into irreducible factors in $F[x]$. If it does not factor completely into linear factors in $F_1[y]$, we may repeat the above process, and thus obtain the

THEOREM 21. *If F is a field and $f(x)$ an element of $F[x]$ of positive degree, there exists a field F' containing F such that $f(x)$ factors into linear factors in $F'[x]$.*

In the classical theory of equations, the so-called "Fundamental Theorem of Algebra" states that every polynomial equation with complex coefficients has a complex root. As an easy consequence, it follows that every polynomial with complex coefficients can be factored into complex factors of the first degree. In abstract algebra,

Theorem 21 is, for many purposes, a simple and adequate substitute for this result.

18. **Rings without unit element.** We have seen earlier that a given ring may or may not have a unit element. In this connection, the following theorem is of some importance:

THEOREM 22. *If R is a ring without unit element, there exists a ring T with unit element which contains R as a subring. More precisely, there exists such a ring T with the same characteristic as R, in which R is not only a subring but actually an ideal.*

Suppose that R has characteristic n, where n is either zero or a positive integer, and let us consider the set S of all symbols of the form $(a, \bar{p})$, where a is in R and $\bar{p}$ is an element of the ring $I/(n)$. If $n = 0$, $I/(n)$ is just the ring of integers; while if $n \neq 0$, $I/(n)$ is the ring of integers modulo n. We shall presently define addition and multiplication in S, but first we observe that if p_1 and p_2 are any two integers in the residue class $\bar{p}$ and a is any element of R, then $p_1a = p_2a$. For $p_1 - p_2$ is an element of the ideal (n), that is, $p_1 - p_2 = kn$ and thus $(p_1 - p_2)a = kna = 0$ since R has characteristic n. Thus pa is uniquely defined by $\bar{p}$ and a. We now define addition and multiplication in S as follows:

$$(a, \bar{p}) + (b, \bar{q}) = (a + b, \bar{p} + \bar{q}),$$

$$(a, \bar{p})(b, \bar{q}) = (ab + qa + pb, \bar{p}\bar{q}).$$

A straightforward calculation will show that S is a ring with unit element $(0, \bar{1})$ and zero $(0, \bar{0})$. It is clear that the characteristic of S is the same as the characteristic of $I/(n)$, in other words, it is precisely n.

Let us now consider the set of all elements of S of the

form $(a, \bar{0})$, where $a \varepsilon R$. Since

$$(a, \bar{0}) - (b, \bar{0}) = (a - b, \bar{0})$$

and

$$(a, \bar{0})(c, \bar{k}) = (ac + ka, \bar{0}), (c, \bar{k})(a, \bar{0}) = (ca + ka, \bar{0}),$$

it follows that this set of elements is an ideal $\mathfrak{r}$ in S. Furthermore, it is easy to verify that the correspondence $a \leftrightarrow (a, \bar{0})$ defines an isomorphism of R and $\mathfrak{r}$. Since S contains a subring isomorphic to R, and R and S have no elements in common, Theorem 20 asserts the existence of a ring T, isomorphic to S, which actually contains R. The theorem is therefore established.

This theorem shows that every ring is a subring of a ring with unit element. Starting with the ring R without a unit element, we have given one method of constructing a ring T meeting the requirements of Theorem 22. However, there may be many other constructions which yield different rings T with the required properties. We shall not go further into these questions but may remark that it is possible to give an example of a ring R without unit element, for which there are an infinite number of rings T_i $(i = 1, 2, \cdots)$, each satisfying all conditions stated in Theorem 22, and *no T_i has a subring isomorphic to T_j if $i \neq j$.*

19. **Rings of quotients.** We assume, in this section, that R is a *commutative* ring, with or without a unit element. If R happens to have a unit element and a is an element of R which has an inverse, a can not be a divisor of zero. However, in general, there may be elements of R which are not divisors of zero and also fail to have inverses. We now investigate the possibility of finding a ring T with unit element which contains R and such that in T all, or a

certain class, of elements of R which are not divisors of zero in R do have inverses in T.

Let M be a set of elements of R which are not divisors of zero in R. We assume further that the set M is a *multiplicative system*, that is, that the product of elements of M is always an element of M. We shall presently construct a ring T containing R such that in T all elements of M have inverses. First, however, we may illustrate the ideas involved. If R is the ring I of integers, then we may choose for M the set of *all* nonzero integers. In this case, our construction of T will yield just the field of rational numbers. As a second example, let us again consider the ring of integers, and choose M as the set of all integers not divisible by the prime 2, that is, the set of all odd integers. In this case, the ring T will consist of all rational numbers of the form m/n, where m and n are integers and n is odd. It can be readily verified that this set is a ring containing I and that in this ring all odd integers have inverses. In like manner, one might choose M to be the set of all integers not divisible by an arbitrary fixed prime, since this set is certainly a multiplicative system.

We now return to the general situation in which R is an arbitrary commutative ring, and M a multiplicative system of elements of R, no element of M being a divisor of zero in R. In general, let us denote elements of R by a, b, c; and elements of M by p, q, r. If p happens to have an inverse in R, R contains elements of the form ap^{-1} (or $p^{-1}a$ since R is commutative), and we may write this in the familiar way, a/p. If p and q both have inverses, we find that

$$a/p = b/q$$

if and only if $aq = bp$.

Let us now consider the set of all symbols of the form

$$(a, p) \qquad\qquad (a \; \varepsilon \; R, \; p \; \varepsilon \; M).$$

Eventually we shall identify these pairs with quotients a/p in a ring containing R and this suggests the following definition. We shall say that (a, p) is *equivalent* to (b, q) if $aq = bp$, in which case we may write

$$(a, p) \sim (b, q).$$

It is easy to verify that this has the three defining properties of an equivalence relation as defined in §6. First of all, it is clear that $(a, p) \sim (a, p)$; also that $(a, p) \sim (b, q)$ implies that $(b, q) \sim (a, p)$. Suppose now that $(a, p) \sim (b, q)$ and $(b, q) \sim (c, r)$. Thus we have $aq = bp$ and $br = cq$. From these equations it follows that $aqr = cpq$ and, since q is not a divisor of zero in R, we see that $ar = cp$; which means that $(a, p) \sim (c, r)$ as required.

With reference to this equivalence relation, we may distribute the elements (a, p) into equivalence classes and denote the class to which (a, p) belongs by $[a, p]$. Thus

$$[a, p] = [b, q]$$

if and only if $aq = bp$. We now let S denote the set of all these equivalence classes and shall make S into a ring by suitable definitions of addition and multiplication. Accordingly, we define

$$(24) \qquad [a, p] + [b, q] = [aq + bp, pq],$$

and

$$(25) \qquad [a, p][b, q] = [ab, pq].$$

It is clear that pq is in M since p and q are in M, and M is assumed to be a multiplicative system. The symbols appearing on the right in (24) and (25) are therefore actually members of the set of equivalence classes under consideration. There is one further step in showing that (24) and (25) really define an addition and multiplication of equivalence classes. The formulas given are based on certain *elements* of each class and we need to show that the sum or product is actually independent of the particular elements used in the definition. Thus, for addition, we need to show that if

$$(26) \qquad [a, p] = [c, r], \qquad [b, q] = [d, s],$$

then

$$(27) \qquad [aq + bp, pq] = [cs + dr, rs].$$

By the definition of equality of equivalence classes, equations (26) mean that

$$(28) \qquad ar = cp, \qquad bs = dq.$$

Now multiply the first of these equations by qs, the second by pr, and add. There results

$$(aq + bp)rs = (cs + dr)pq,$$

which, however, is just what is needed to establish (27); and thus (24) actually defines an addition of equivalence classes. To prove the corresponding property for multiplication we multiply corresponding members of equations (28). Thus, we see that

$$arbs = cpdq,$$

which implies that

$$[ab, pq] = [cd, rs],$$

as required.

The next step in our construction is to show that S is a ring with respect to the definitions (24) and (25) of addition and multiplication, respectively. To prove the associative law of addition, we note that

$$([a, p] + [b, q]) + [c, r] = [aq + bp, pq] + [c, r]$$
$$= [aqr + bpr + cpq, pqr],$$

and also that

$$[a, p] + ([b, q] + [c, r]) = [a, p] + [br + cq, qr]$$
$$= [aqr + bpr + cpq, pqr].$$

The commutative law of addition and the associative law of multiplication are obviously satisfied. Furthermore, since $[bp^2, qp^2] = [b, q]$, it is easily verified that the equation

$$[a, p] + [x, y] = [b, q]$$

has the solution

$$[x, y] = [bp - aq, pq].$$

Finally, we prove the distributive laws. Since R is assumed to be a commutative ring, it follows from the definition of multiplication in S that S is also commutative, and we accordingly need to prove only one of the distributive laws. This is accomplished by the following calculation:

$$[a, p]([b, q] + [c, r]) = [a, p][br + cq, qr] = [abr + acq, pqr],$$
$$[a, p][b, q] + [a, p][c, r] = [ab, pq] + [ac, pr]$$
$$= [abpr + acpq, p^2qr].$$

However, the two right sides are equal inasmuch as

$$(abr + acq)p^2qr = (abpr + acpq)pqr.$$

This completes the proof that S is a ring.

We proceed to show that S contains a subring isomorphic to R. First we observe that if p and q are elements of M, a any element of R, then $[ap, p] = [aq, q]$. Furthermore, if $[ap, p] = [bp, p]$, it follows that $ap^2 = bp^2$ and, since p is not a divisor of zero, this implies that $a = b$. From this, it is clear that

$$a \leftrightarrow [ap, p],$$

where p is any element of M, defines a one-to-one correspondence between elements of R and a set S_1 of elements of S, and S_1 is independent of the choice of p. We now see that

$$a + b \leftrightarrow [(a + b)p, p] = [(a + b)p^2, p^2]$$
$$= [ap, p] + [bp, p],$$

and

$$ab \leftrightarrow [abp, p] = [abp^2, p^2] = [ap, p][bp, p].$$

This shows that S_1 is isomorphic to R and, by Theorem 20, we may let T be the ring isomorphic to S in which the elements of S_1 are actually replaced by the corresponding elements of R. Thus, in T, we write a in place of $[ap, p]$.

It is clear that T has a unit element, namely, the element $[p, p]$ where p is any element of M. Furthermore, in T, the equation

$$p[x, y] = [p, p]$$

has the unique solution

$$[x, y] = [p, p^2].$$

Hence in T, p has an inverse. As a further fact of interest, we see that the equation

$$p[x, y] = a$$

has the unique solution $[a, p]$. Hence it is justified to write $[a, p]$ in the more familiar form ap^{-1} or a/p. Thus the elements of T are precisely all quotients a/p, where $a \, \varepsilon \, R$,

$p \ \varepsilon \ M$; it being understood that ap/p is to be identified with a. We have therefore proved the following result:

THEOREM 23. *Let R be a commutative ring and M a multiplicative system of elements of R which contains no divisor of zero. Then the set T of all quotients*

$$a/p \qquad\qquad (a \ \varepsilon \ R, \ p \ \varepsilon \ M)$$

is a ring which contains R as a subring, and in T all elements of M have inverses.

If R is an integral domain, we may choose for M the set of all nonzero elements of R. In this case, if $a \neq 0$, $b \neq 0$, the inverse of a/b is b/a, and we have the important

COROLLARY 1. *An integral domain R may be imbedded in a field of quotients, that is, a field whose elements are of the form a/b, where a and b are elements of R and $b \neq 0$.*

As an illustration of this corollary, we remark that by starting with the ring of integers (or the ring of even integers for that matter) the field of quotients thus obtained is just the familiar field of rational numbers.

If p is not a divisor of zero in the ring R, we may choose M to be the set p^i $(i = 1, 2, \cdots)$, since this is a multiplicative system containing no divisor of zero. We thus obtain

COROLLARY 2. *If p is not a divisor of zero in the commutative ring R, there exists a ring T containing R as a subring, whose elements are of the form a/p^i, where $a \ \varepsilon \ R$ and i is a positive integer.*

REFERENCES

Albert [1], Chapters I, II; Birkhoff and MacLane [1], Chapter II; Bourbaki [1], §9; Dubreil [1], Chapter V(A); MacDuffee [2], Chapter V; van der Waerden [1], Chapter III.

For different ways of imbedding a ring in a ring with unit element see Brown and McCoy [1] and the references there given.

Rings of quotients, in the general form as presented in §19, are introduced in Grell [1]. The most important case, that of imbedding an integral domain in a field of quotients, is treated in all the texts listed above. An exposition of the problem of imbedding a noncommutative ring in a ring of quotients will be found in Dubreil [1], Chapter V(A).

PRIME IDEALS IN COMMUTATIVE RINGS

20. Prime ideals. One of the most important properties of a prime integer p is that a product of two integers is divisible by p only if at least one of the integers is divisible by p. In the notation of principal ideals, this can be restated as follows. If p is a prime, then $n_1 n_2 \equiv 0(p)$ implies that $n_1 \equiv 0(p)$ or $n_2 \equiv 0(p)$, or both. Now if R is an arbitrary *commutative* ring, an ideal $\mathfrak{p}$ in R is said to be a *prime ideal* if and only if $ab \equiv 0(\mathfrak{p})$ implies that $a \equiv 0(\mathfrak{p})$ or $b \equiv 0(\mathfrak{p})$, or both. Thus the prime ideals in I are precisely the ideals (p), where p is a prime, together with the ideal (0) and the ideal I. In any commutative ring R, it is obvious that the ideal R is always prime; and the ideal (0) is a prime ideal if and only if R has no proper divisors of zero.

It may be remarked that the definition of a prime ideal can be stated in other convenient forms which are, however, logically equivalent to that given above. Thus, an ideal $\mathfrak{p}$ is a prime ideal if and only if $ab \equiv 0(\mathfrak{p})$ and $a \not\equiv 0(\mathfrak{p})$ imply that $b \equiv 0(\mathfrak{p})$. Or, an ideal $\mathfrak{p}$ is a prime ideal if and only if $a \not\equiv 0(\mathfrak{p})$ and $b \not\equiv 0(\mathfrak{p})$ imply that $ab \not\equiv 0(\mathfrak{p})$.

Throughout this chapter, we shall find it convenient to consider that the *void set*, that is, the set which contains no elements, is a multiplicative system. However, in accordance with our definition of ideal we shall continue to require that an *ideal* must contain at least one element. If A is a set of elements of R, let us denote by $C(A)$ the set of elements of R not in A, the so-called *complement* of A in R. The last form of the definition of prime ideal given above then states that *the ideal* $\mathfrak{p}$ *is a prime ideal if and only if* $C(\mathfrak{p})$ *is a multiplicative system.* Our agreement to consider the void set as a multiplicative system is necessary to take care of the special case in which $\mathfrak{p} = R$, as then $C(\mathfrak{p})$ is the void set.

We now give some further examples of prime ideals. If F is a field, it has been shown in Theorem 13 that every ideal in the polynomial ring $F[x]$ is principal. The results of §9 then show that if $p(x)$ has positive degree, the ideal $(p(x))$ in $F[x]$ is a prime ideal if and only if $p(x)$ is irreducible in $F[x]$. The zero ideal is also prime since $F[x]$ has no proper divisors of zero.

These remarks, together with the results of §16, show that in the rings I and $F[x]$ every nonzero prime ideal is a maximal ideal, or is the entire ring. We shall presently show that this is not true in all rings. Consider the ideal (x) in the ring $I[x, y]$ of polynomials in two indeterminates, with integral coefficients. An arbitrary element f of $I[x, y]$ may be considered as a polynomial in x with coefficients in $I[y]$, that is, we may write

$$f = f_0 x^n + f_1 x^{n-1} + \cdots + f_n ,$$

where the f_i are elements of $I[y]$. Then it is clear that $f \equiv 0(x)$ if and only if $f_n = 0$. To prove that (x) is a prime ideal, let f and

$$g = g_0 x^m + g_1 x^{m-1} + \cdots + g_m \quad (g_i \ \varepsilon \ I[y])$$

be elements of $I[x, y]$ such that $fg \equiv 0(x)$, $g \not\equiv 0(x)$. This means, however, that $f_n g_m = 0$, $g_m \neq 0$. Since $I[y]$ has no proper divisors of zero, it follows that $f_n = 0$. Thus $f = 0(x)$, and (x) is therefore a prime ideal. It is obvious that (y) is also a prime ideal in $I[x, y]$.

Let us next consider the ideal (x, y) in $I[x, y]$. It is easy to show, by calculations similar to those following Theorem 13, that the elements of this ideal are just the elements of

$I[x, y]$ with zero constant terms. Since the constant term of fg is the product of the constant terms of f and of g, it follows that $fg \equiv 0(x, y)$ implies that $f \equiv 0(x, y)$ or $g \equiv 0(x, y)$, and thus (x, y) is a prime ideal.

The elements of the ideal $(x, y, 2)$ in $I[x, y]$ are just the elements of $I[x, y]$ with *even* constant terms. The reader may verify that this is also a prime ideal. In $I[x, y]$ we have, therefore,

$$(x) \subset (x, y) \subset (x, y, 2),$$

where all these ideals are prime. This makes it clear that a prime ideal may or may not be a maximal ideal. As a matter of fact, it is not difficult to show that $(x, y, 2)$ *is* a maximal ideal in $I[x, y]$.

At this point we may remark that in an arbitrary commutative ring R *an ideal $\mathfrak{p}$ is a prime ideal if and only if the residue class ring $R/\mathfrak{p}$ has no proper divisors of zero.* Let $\mathfrak{p}$ be a prime ideal in R, and suppose that $\bar{a}\bar{b} = 0$ in the ring $R/\mathfrak{p}$. This means simply that $ab \equiv 0(\mathfrak{p})$ and, since $\mathfrak{p}$ is a prime ideal, we must have $a \equiv 0(\mathfrak{p})$ or $b \equiv 0(\mathfrak{p})$. That is, in $R/\mathfrak{p}$, either $\bar{a} = 0$ or $\bar{b} = 0$; hence $R/\mathfrak{p}$ has no proper divisors of zero. The converse may be shown by reversing these steps.

21. The radical of an ideal. Let n be a positive integer with the distinct prime factors $p_1, p_2, \cdots, p_k$. If m is any integer, it is obvious that some positive integral power of m will be divisible by n if and only if m is divisible by each of the primes $p_1, p_2, \cdots, p_k$. In other words, some positive integral power of m will be in the ideal (n) if and only if m is in each of the prime ideals $(p_1), (p_2), \cdots, (p_k)$; that is, if and only if m is in the intersection of these prime ideals. Furthermore, except for the prime ideal I, these prime ideals are the *only* prime ideals which contain n, or the ideal (n). Since every ideal in I is a principal ideal, these remarks show that if $\mathfrak{a}$ is any nonzero ideal in I, then $m^i \ \varepsilon \ \mathfrak{a}$, for some positive integer i, if and only if m is in the intersection of all prime ideals in I which contain $\mathfrak{a}$. Since every ideal contains 0, and the intersection of *all* prime ideals in I is (0), this statement is also true for the zero ideal. It may be verified that similar results hold for the ring $F[x]$, where F is a field. In this case, the irreducible elements play a role corresponding to that of the primes in I.

Now let R be an arbitrary commutative ring and $\mathfrak{a}$ an ideal in R. We denote by $\mathfrak{r}$ the set of all elements a of R such that $a^i \ \varepsilon \ \mathfrak{a}$ for some positive integer i, depending on a. It is easy to show that $\mathfrak{r}$ is an ideal. In the first place, suppose that $a \ \varepsilon \ \mathfrak{r}$, $b \ \varepsilon \ \mathfrak{r}$, that is, $a^i \ \varepsilon \ \mathfrak{a}$, $b^j \ \varepsilon \ \mathfrak{a}$. Then $(a - b)^{i+j-1}$ can be expressed as a sum of terms each one of which contains as a factor either a^i or b^j, hence $(a - b)^{i+j-1}$ is in $\mathfrak{a}$, and thus $a - b \ \varepsilon \ \mathfrak{r}$. Also, if $r \ \varepsilon \ R$, then

$$(ra)^i = r^i a^i \ \varepsilon \ \mathfrak{a},$$

and thus $ra \ \varepsilon \ \mathfrak{r}$. This shows that $\mathfrak{r}$ is an ideal which we shall call the *radical* of the ideal $\mathfrak{a}$. In terms of this concept, we showed above that, in the ring I, the radical of an ideal $\mathfrak{a}$ is the intersection of all prime ideals containing $\mathfrak{a}$. It is an interesting and important fact that this is also true in an *arbitrary* commutative ring, as will follow from our more precise Theorem 24. However, the proof is more difficult in the general case, and will have to be postponed until suitable methods have been developed.

It is obvious that if $\mathfrak{r}$ is the radical of $\mathfrak{a}$, then $\mathfrak{a} \subseteq \mathfrak{r}$. We may also point out that $\mathfrak{a}$ *and* $\mathfrak{r}$ *are contained in precisely the same prime ideals*, in other words, if $\mathfrak{p}$ is a prime ideal such that $\mathfrak{a} \subseteq \mathfrak{p}$, then $\mathfrak{a} \subseteq \mathfrak{r} \subseteq \mathfrak{p}$. This follows from the observation that if $a \ \varepsilon \ \mathfrak{r}$, then $a^i \ \varepsilon \ \mathfrak{a}$ and therefore $a^i \ \varepsilon \ \mathfrak{p}$. But since $\mathfrak{p}$ is a prime ideal, this implies that $a \ \varepsilon \ \mathfrak{p}$, and hence $\mathfrak{r} \subseteq \mathfrak{p}$. As a special case of this result, it follows that *a prime ideal coincides with its radical.*

An element a of the commutative ring R is said to be *nilpotent* if $a^i = 0$ for some positive integer i. The set of all nilpotent elements is merely the radical of the zero ideal, and hence is an ideal. It is now easy to verify that *if $\mathfrak{r}$ is the radical of an ideal* $\mathfrak{a}$, *the residue class ring $R/\mathfrak{r}$ has no nonzero nilpotent elements.* For suppose that $\bar{a}$ is a nilpotent element of $R/\mathfrak{r}$. Then, for some positive integer i, $\bar{a}^i = 0$, that is, $a^i \,\varepsilon\, \mathfrak{r}$. Hence, for some positive integer j, $(a^i)^j \,\varepsilon\, \mathfrak{a}$. This shows, however, that $a \,\varepsilon\, \mathfrak{r}$ and hence that $\bar{a} = 0$.

22. A maximum principle. Let $\mathfrak{M}$ be an arbitrary set of elements of any kind, and let us denote subsets of $\mathfrak{M}$ by A, B, C, $\cdots$. In all our applications, $\mathfrak{M}$ will be a set of elements of a ring but, in this section, we make no restrictions on $\mathfrak{M}$. By the notation, $A \subseteq B$, we shall mean that all elements of A are also elements of B, and we maysay that A *is contained in* B or that B *contains* A. Of course, this is consistent with the notation and terminology previously introduced for ideals. By the *union* of any finite or infinite number of subsets of $\mathfrak{M}$ we mean the subset of $\mathfrak{M}$ which consists of all elements that are in at least one of the given subsets.

We now let $\mathfrak{A}$ denote a system of one or more subsets of $\mathfrak{M}$, each of which may conveniently be called an *element* of $\mathfrak{A}$. An element M of $\mathfrak{A}$ is said to be *maximal in* $\mathfrak{A}$ if $M \subseteq A$ for *any* element A of $\mathfrak{A}$ implies that $M = A$ or, in other words, if there is no element of $\mathfrak{A}$ which contains M as a proper subset.*

---

* According to this terminology, a *maximal ideal in R,* as defined in §16, is maximal in the set of all ideals in R other than R itself.

The maximum principle, which we shall presently state, asserts that under certain conditions $\mathfrak{A}$ contains at least one maximal element. Before stating the conditions, let us illustrate these concepts by some simple examples. For the present, let $\mathfrak{M}'$ be the set of all positive integers, and $\mathfrak{A}_1$ the system of all nonvoid subsets of $\mathfrak{M}'$ which contain at most three elements of $\mathfrak{M}'$. Here every set of three elements is clearly maximal, and hence $\mathfrak{A}_1$ has maximal elements. However, if we consider the system $\mathfrak{A}_2$ of all *finite* subsets of $\mathfrak{M}'$, the situation is quite different in that there is no maximal element of $\mathfrak{A}_2$. As a further example, let us denote by $\mathfrak{A}_3$ the system of all subsets A of $\mathfrak{M}'$ with the property that if i is in A, then j is in A for all positive integers $j < i$. In this case, an element of $\mathfrak{A}_3$ consists of all integers less than some fixed positive integer, or is the set $\mathfrak{M}'$ of all positive integers. Clearly the set $\mathfrak{M}'$ is a maximal element of $\mathfrak{A}_3$.

We now return to the general situation and make the following additional definitions. If $\mathfrak{L}$ is a system of one or more subsets of $\mathfrak{M}$ with the property that for any elements L_1 and L_2 of $\mathfrak{L}$ either $L_1 \subseteq L_2$ or $L_2 \subseteq L_1$, then $\mathfrak{L}$ is a *linear* system. If all elements of $\mathfrak{L}$ are also elements of $\mathfrak{A}$, $\mathfrak{L}$ is a *linear subsystem* of $\mathfrak{A}$. We may now formulate the following

MAXIMUM PRINCIPLE. *If the union of each linear subsystem of $\mathfrak{A}$ is an element of $\mathfrak{A}$, then $\mathfrak{A}$ has a maximal element.*

In the literature, this is usually referred to as Zorn's Lemma. It is logically equivalent to the Axiom of Choice, or to the possibility of well-ordering every set. However, we shall simply regard the Maximum Principle *as an axiom*, and henceforth use it freely.

Let us return to the illustrative examples given above,

and verify that the Maximum Principle yields results consistent with what we have already noted. It will be convenient to denote by $\{i_1, i_2, \cdots, i_n\}$ the subset of $\mathfrak{M}'$ consisting of the integers $i_1, i_2, \cdots, i_n$. Clearly a linear subsystem of $\mathfrak{A}_1$ can contain no more than three different subsets; a typical one consists of the three subsets $\{i\}$, $\{i, j\}$, $\{i, j, k\}$, where i, j, k are distinct positive integers. The union of these three subsets is just the set $\{i, j, k\}$ which is itself an element of the given linear subsystem, and therefore an element of $\mathfrak{A}_1$. Thus the union of each linear subsystem of $\mathfrak{A}_1$ is an element of $\mathfrak{A}_1$, and the Maximum Principle asserts the existence of a maximal element of $\mathfrak{A}_1$. Let us turn to the system $\mathfrak{A}_2$, and consider the set $\mathfrak{L}$ of all subsets of the form $\{1, 2, \cdots, i\}$, where i is a positive integer. This is a linear system and in fact a linear subsystem of $\mathfrak{A}_2$. Since every positive integer occurs in some element of $\mathfrak{L}$, it is clear that the union of all elements of $\mathfrak{L}$ is not a finite set and hence is not an element of $\mathfrak{A}_2$. Thus the Maximum Principle does not apply, and we have already observed that in this case there is no maximal element. The reader may verify that the union of each linear subsystem of $\mathfrak{A}_3$ is an element of $\mathfrak{A}_3$, and thus the conclusion of the Maximum Principle is consistent with our previous observation that $\mathfrak{A}_3$ does have a maximal element.

Clearly, these are examples of such a simple nature that the Maximum Principle gives no information not already evident. However, they may help to clarify the concepts as well as the notation which will be used in applications of this principle.

In all our applications, the set $\mathfrak{M}$ will be a set of elements of a ring R, and the elements of $\mathfrak{A}$ will be either ideals in R or multiplicative systems of elements ·of R. We may now make a few preliminary remarks by way of preparation for later use. First, we shall show that *the union U of any linear system $\mathfrak{L}$ of ideals in R is an ideal in R.* If a, b are arbitrary elements of U, r any element of R, we have only to show that $a - b \,\varepsilon\, U$, $ar \,\varepsilon\, U$, and $ra \,\varepsilon\, U$. Since a and b are in U, it follows that $a \,\varepsilon\, L_1$, $b \,\varepsilon\, L_2$, where L_1 and L_2 are elements (ideals) of $\mathfrak{L}$. Now since $\mathfrak{L}$ is a linear system, we know that either $L_1 \subseteq L_2$ or $L_2 \subseteq L_1$, and suppose for definiteness that $L_1 \subseteq L_2$. Then $a \,\varepsilon\, L_2$, $b \,\varepsilon\, L_2$ and, since L_2 is an ideal, we must have $a - b \,\varepsilon\, L_2$, $ar \,\varepsilon\, L_2$, and $ra \,\varepsilon\, L_2$. However, $L_2 \subseteq U$, and therefore these elements are in U, and the proof is completed.

A similar argument applies to the case in which the elements of $\mathfrak{L}$ are multiplicative systems of elements of R. We now show that, in this case, *the union U of all elements of $\mathfrak{L}$ is a multiplicative system of elements of R.* Suppose that c and d are elements of U, therefore each of these is an element of R contained in a multiplicative system in $\mathfrak{L}$. That is, $c \,\varepsilon\, M_1$, $d \,\varepsilon\, M_2$, where M_1 and M_2 are in $\mathfrak{L}$. As in the preceding case, we may assume that $M_1 \subseteq M_2$. Hence $c \,\varepsilon\, M_2$, $d \,\varepsilon\, M_2$, and therefore $cd \,\varepsilon\, M_2$ since M_2 is a multiplicative system. It follows that $cd \,\varepsilon\, U$, and hence that U is itself a multiplicative system of elements of R.

23. **Minimal prime ideals belonging to an ideal.** Let $\mathfrak{a}$ be an ideal in the commutative ring R. A prime ideal $\mathfrak{p}$ in R is said to be a *minimal prime ideal belonging to* $\mathfrak{a}$ if $\mathfrak{a} \subseteq \mathfrak{p}$ and there is no prime ideal $\mathfrak{p}'$ in R such that $\mathfrak{a} \subseteq \mathfrak{p}' \subset \mathfrak{p}$.

In the ring of integers, the minimal prime ideals belonging to the nonzero ideal (n) are merely the prime ideals (p), where p is a prime divisor of n. In this case, then, the minimal prime ideals belonging to (n) are precisely the prime ideals which contain (n). This, however, is not true in all rings, as can be seen by a consideration of the ideal (x^2y, xy^2) in the ring $I[x, y]$. It is clear that

$$(x^2y, xy^2) \subset (x) \subset (x, y) \subset (x, y, 2)$$

and the last three of these ideals are prime, as shown in §20. Actually, (x) is a minimal prime ideal belonging to (x^2y, xy^2). For suppose that $\mathfrak{p}'$ is a prime ideal such that

$$(x^2y, \; xy^2) \subseteq \mathfrak{p}' \subset (x).$$

Since $x^2y \equiv 0(\mathfrak{p}')$, it follows that either $x \equiv 0(\mathfrak{p}')$ or $y \equiv 0(\mathfrak{p}')$. But $y \not\equiv 0(x)$ and therefore $y \not\equiv 0(\mathfrak{p}')$; hence we must have $x \equiv 0(\mathfrak{p}')$. Thus $\mathfrak{p}' \supseteq (x)$, which violates the assumption that $\mathfrak{p}' \subset (x)$. In like manner, it can be shown that (y) is also a minimal prime ideal belonging to the ideal (x^2y, xy^2). Furthermore, the argument shows that any prime ideal containing (x^2y, xy^2) contains either (x) or (y); hence these are the *only* minimal prime ideals belonging to (x^2y, xy^2). As an illustration of the next theorem, we may point out that an element of $I[x, y]$ is in the radical of (x^2y, xy^2) if and only if it has both x and y as factors, that is, if and only if it is an element of both the prime ideals (x) and (y).

The primary purpose of this section is to prove the important

THEOREM 24. *The radical $\mathfrak{r}$ of an ideal $\mathfrak{a}$ in the commutative ring R is the intersection of all minimal prime ideals belonging to $\mathfrak{a}$.*

We shall prove several lemmas which will lead to a proof of this theorem. If two sets of elements of a ring have no element in common, it will be convenient to say that either of these sets does not *meet* the other.

LEMMA 1. *Let $\mathfrak{a}$ be an ideal in the commutative ring R, and M a multiplicative system of elements of R which does not meet $\mathfrak{a}$. Then M is contained in a maximal multiplicative system M^* which does not meet $\mathfrak{a}$, that is, if N is a multiplicative system such that $M^* \subset N$, then N contains an element of $\mathfrak{a}$.*

In the notation used in the statement of the Maximum Principle, let $\mathfrak{A}$ be the set of all multiplicative systems in R which contain M but do not meet $\mathfrak{a}$. If $\mathfrak{L}$ is a linear subsystem of $\mathfrak{A}$, it was shown in the preceding section that the union U of all elements of $\mathfrak{L}$ is a multiplicative system. Clearly U contains M and does not meet $\mathfrak{a}$, hence is an element of $\mathfrak{A}$. The Maximum Principle then asserts that $\mathfrak{A}$ has a maximal element M^*, as required in the statement of the lemma. If then M^* is properly contained in a multiplicative system N, N can not be in $\mathfrak{A}$ and hence must contain an element of $\mathfrak{a}$.

LEMMA 2. *Let M be a multiplicative system in the commutative ring R, and $\mathfrak{a}$ an ideal which does not meet M. Then $\mathfrak{a}$ is contained in a maximal ideal $\mathfrak{p}^*$ which does not meet M, that is, if $\mathfrak{n}$ is an ideal such that $\mathfrak{p}^* \subset \mathfrak{n}$, then $\mathfrak{n}$ contains an element of M. Such an ideal $\mathfrak{p}^*$ is necessarily prime.*

It has already been shown that the union of a linear system of ideals is an ideal, hence the existence of an ideal $\mathfrak{p}^*$ with the required maximal property follows from an application of the Maximum Principle to the set $\mathfrak{A}$ of all ideals which contain $\mathfrak{a}$ but do not meet M. There remains to show that $\mathfrak{p}^*$ is necessarily a prime ideal. To this end, let us assume that $a \not\equiv 0(\mathfrak{p}^*)$, $b \not\equiv 0(\mathfrak{p}^*)$, and show that $ab \not\equiv 0(\mathfrak{p}^*)$. Since $a \not\equiv 0(\mathfrak{p}^*)$, it is clear that $\mathfrak{p}^* \subset (\mathfrak{p}^*, a)$, and because of the maximal property of $\mathfrak{p}^*$ this implies that $(\mathfrak{p}^*, a)$ contains an element m_1 of M. Hence

$$m_1 = p_1 + r_1 a + i_1 a \qquad (p_1 \; \varepsilon \; \mathfrak{p}^*, \; r_1 \; \varepsilon \; R, \; i_1 \; \varepsilon \; I),$$

since all elements of $(\mathfrak{p}^*, a)$ are expressible in this form. Similarly, $(\mathfrak{p}^*, b)$ contains an element m_2 of M, and

$$m_2 = p_2 + r_2 b + i_2 b \qquad (p_2 \; \varepsilon \; \mathfrak{p}^*, \; r_2 \; \varepsilon \; R, \; i_2 \; \varepsilon \; I).$$

Since M is a multiplicative system which does not meet

$\mathfrak{p}^*$, it follows that $m_1 m_2 \not\equiv 0(\mathfrak{p}^*)$. But from the above expressions for m_1 and m_2 it is clear that

$$m_1 m_2 \equiv sab + jab(\mathfrak{p}^*),$$

where $s \; \varepsilon \; R$, $j \; \varepsilon \; I$. Therefore $ab \not\equiv 0(\mathfrak{p}^*)$, and this completes the proof of the lemma.

We have already pointed out that an ideal $\mathfrak{p}$ in R is a prime ideal if and only if the complement $C(\mathfrak{p})$ of $\mathfrak{p}$ in R is a multiplicative system. We shall now prove

LEMMA 3. *A set $\mathfrak{p}$ of elements of the commutative ring R is a minimal prime ideal belonging to the ideal $\mathfrak{a}$ if and only if $C(\mathfrak{p})$ is a maximal multiplicative system which does not meet $\mathfrak{a}$.*

First, let $\mathfrak{p}$ be a set of elements such that $M = C(\mathfrak{p})$ is a maximal multiplicative system which does not meet $\mathfrak{a}$. By Lemma 2, there is a prime ideal $\mathfrak{p}^*$ which contains $\mathfrak{a}$ and does not meet M. Hence $C(\mathfrak{p}^*)$ is a multiplicative system which does not meet $\mathfrak{a}$ and contains M. From the maximal property of M, it follows that $C(\mathfrak{p}^*) = M = C(\mathfrak{p})$, and hence that $\mathfrak{p} = \mathfrak{p}^*$. Also this maximal property shows that there is no prime ideal $\mathfrak{p}_1$ such that $\mathfrak{a} \subseteq \mathfrak{p}_1 \subset \mathfrak{p}$, as otherwise $C(\mathfrak{p}_1)$ would be a multiplicative system which does not meet $\mathfrak{a}$ and contains M as proper subset. We have therefore shown that $\mathfrak{p}$ is a minimal prime ideal belonging to $\mathfrak{a}$.

For the converse, suppose that $\mathfrak{p}$ is a minimal prime ideal belonging to $\mathfrak{a}$. Then $M = C(\mathfrak{p})$ is a multiplicative system which does not meet $\mathfrak{a}$, and Lemma 1 shows the existence of a maximal multiplicative system M' which contains M and does not meet $\mathfrak{a}$. By the case just proved, $C(M') = \mathfrak{p}'$ is a minimal prime ideal belonging to $\mathfrak{a}$. But since $M' \supseteq M$, it follows that $\mathfrak{p}' \subseteq \mathfrak{p}$, and the minimal property of $\mathfrak{p}$ then shows that $\mathfrak{p} = \mathfrak{p}'$. Hence $M = M'$, and $C(\mathfrak{p}) = M$ is a maximal multiplicative system which does not meet $\mathfrak{a}$.

It is now easy to establish Theorem 24. It was pointed out in §21 that any prime ideal which contains the ideal $\mathfrak{a}$ also contains its radical $\mathfrak{r}$; hence $\mathfrak{r}$ is *contained in* the intersection of all minimal prime ideals belonging to $\mathfrak{a}$. We shall complete the proof by showing that if a is an element of R not in $\mathfrak{r}$, then there is a minimal prime ideal belonging to $\mathfrak{a}$ which does not contain a. If a is such an element, then the set M of all elements of the form a^i ($i = 1, 2, \cdots$) is a multiplicative system which does not meet $\mathfrak{a}$. By Lemma 1, M is contained in a maximal multiplicative system M^* which does not meet $\mathfrak{a}$. Since $a \, \varepsilon \, M^*$, a is not in $C(M^*)$ which, by Lemma 3, is a minimal prime ideal belonging to $\mathfrak{a}$. Thus a is not in the intersection of all minimal prime ideals belonging to $\mathfrak{a}$, and this completes the proof of the theorem.

THEOREM 25. *Any prime ideal containing the ideal $\mathfrak{a}$ contains a minimal prime ideal belonging to $\mathfrak{a}$.*

This follows easily from Lemmas 1 and 3. If $\mathfrak{p}$ is a prime ideal containing $\mathfrak{a}$, then $C(\mathfrak{p})$, being a multiplicative system which does not meet $\mathfrak{a}$, is contained in a maximal multiplicative system M^* which does not meet $\mathfrak{a}$. It follows that $C(M^*)$ is a minimal prime ideal belonging to $\mathfrak{a}$, and $C(M^*) \subseteq \mathfrak{p}$ since $C(\mathfrak{p}) \subseteq M^*$.

24. **Maximal prime ideals belonging to an ideal.** In this section we shall study another system of prime ideals associated with a given ideal $\mathfrak{a}$ in a commutative ring R. First, however, we introduce some necessary preliminary concepts.

An element b of R may be said to be *related to* the ideal $\mathfrak{a}$ if there exists an element r of R *not in* $\mathfrak{a}$ such that

$br \equiv 0(\mathfrak{a})$. If no such element r exists, b is *unrelated to* $\mathfrak{a}$.*
In view of this definition, b is unrelated to $\mathfrak{a}$ if and only if
the congruence $bx \equiv 0(\mathfrak{a})$ implies that $x \equiv 0(\mathfrak{a})$. It is
clear that, except in the trivial case in which $\mathfrak{a} = R$,
every element of $\mathfrak{a}$ is related to $\mathfrak{a}$; for if $a \equiv 0(\mathfrak{a})$ and r is
any element of R not in $\mathfrak{a}$, then $ar \equiv 0(\mathfrak{a})$. We assume,
henceforth, that $\mathfrak{a} \neq R$.

We shall say that an *ideal* $\mathfrak{b}$ is *related to* $\mathfrak{a}$ if every
element of $\mathfrak{b}$ is related to $\mathfrak{a}$; otherwise, $\mathfrak{b}$ is *unrelated to* $\mathfrak{a}$.
It is easy to see that *the radical* $\mathfrak{r}$ *of* $\mathfrak{a}$ *is related to* $\mathfrak{a}$. Suppose that $d \equiv 0(\mathfrak{r})$, that is, $d^i \equiv 0(\mathfrak{a})$, for some positive
integer i. If $i = 1$, d is an element of $\mathfrak{a}$ and therefore
related to $\mathfrak{a}$. If $i > 1$ and is chosen in such a way that
$d^{i-1} \not\equiv 0(\mathfrak{a})$, then $d(d^{i-1}) \equiv 0(\mathfrak{a})$ shows that d is related to
$\mathfrak{a}$. Thus every element of $\mathfrak{r}$ is related to $\mathfrak{a}$, and hence $\mathfrak{r}$ is
related to $\mathfrak{a}$.

As a simple illustration of these concepts, let m and n be
nonzero elements of the ring I of integers. By definition,
n is related to the ideal (m) if and only if there exists an
integer k, not in (m), such that $kn \equiv 0(m)$. It follows at
once that n is related to (m) if and only if n is divisible
by some prime divisor of m. Incidentally, this shows that
in the ring I the ideal (n) is related to the ideal (m) if and
only if (m) is related to (n). However, in other rings it
may happen that $\mathfrak{a}$ is related to $\mathfrak{b}$ with $\mathfrak{b}$ unrelated to $\mathfrak{a}$.
As an example of this, let $\mathfrak{a} = (x)$, $\mathfrak{b} = (x, y)$ in the ring
$I[x, y]$. If $yf \equiv 0(x)$, then $f \equiv 0(x)$, so that y is unrelated
to $\mathfrak{a}$, and therefore $\mathfrak{b}$ is unrelated to $\mathfrak{a}$. However, $\mathfrak{a} \subset \mathfrak{b}$
so that all elements of $\mathfrak{a}$ are related to $\mathfrak{b}$, that is, $\mathfrak{a}$ is related
to $\mathfrak{b}$.

---

* In the literature, one finds "b is prime (not prime) to $\mathfrak{a}$"
in place of our "b is unrelated (related) to $\mathfrak{a}$." However, our terminology seems to clarify matters somewhat in that it avoids any
possible confusion with other connotations of the word "prime."

In any ring R, the elements related to the ideal (0) are just the divisors of zero; all other elements are unrelated to (0). Thus we have a generalization of the concept of divisor of zero. In fact, it may be noted that an element c of R is related to the ideal $\mathfrak{a}$ if and only if the element $\bar{c}$ of the residue class ring $R/\mathfrak{a}$ is a divisor of zero in $R/\mathfrak{a}$.

As a further illustration, let us again consider the ideal $\mathfrak{a} = (x^2y, xy^2)$ in the ring $I[x, y]$. It is easy to see that if f is an element of $I[x, y]$ with zero constant term, then $xyf \equiv 0(\mathfrak{a})$, $xy \not\equiv 0(\mathfrak{a})$, and hence f is related to $\mathfrak{a}$. It will now be shown that all other elements are unrelated to $\mathfrak{a}$. If g is an element of $I[x, y]$, it is clear that we may write

$$g \equiv a_0 + xg_1(x) + yg_2(y) + a_3xy \ (\mathfrak{a}),$$

where a_0 is the constant term of g, $a_3 \ \varepsilon \ I$, $g_1(x) \ \varepsilon \ I[x]$, $g_2(y) \ \varepsilon \ I[y]$. Furthermore, $g \equiv 0(\mathfrak{a})$ if and only if $a_0 = a_3 = g_1(x) = g_2(y) = 0$. If h is another element of $I[x, y]$ and

$$h \equiv b_0 + xh_1(x) + yh_2(y) + b_3xy \ (\mathfrak{a}),$$

we see that

$$\begin{aligned}
gh \equiv a_0b_0 &+ [a_0h_1(x) + xg_1(x)h_1(x) + b_0g_1(x)]x \\
&+ [a_0h_2(y) + yg_2(y)h_2(y) + b_0g_2(y)]y \\
&+ xy[a_0b_3 + a_3b_0 + g_1(x)h_2(y) + g_2(y)h_1(x)](\mathfrak{a}).
\end{aligned}$$

Now suppose that g has nonzero constant term a_0 and that $gh \equiv 0(\mathfrak{a})$. We shall show that h must be in $\mathfrak{a}$, and hence that g is unrelated to $\mathfrak{a}$. Since $gh \equiv 0(\mathfrak{a})$, it follows, in particular, that $a_0b_0 = 0$, and since $a_0 \neq 0$ we must have $b_0 = 0$. Next,

$$a_0h_1(x) + xg_1(x)h_1(x) = 0,$$

that is,

$$[a_0 + xg_1(x)]h_1(x) = 0.$$

Since $a_0 \neq 0$, the first term is different from zero, and hence $h_1(x) = 0$ since $I[x, y]$ has no proper divisors of zero. Similarly, it follows that $h_2(y) = 0$, and then a consideration of the last part of the expression for gh shows that $a_0 b_3 = 0$. Thus $b_3 = 0$, and we have shown that $h \equiv 0(\mathfrak{a})$, that is, that g is unrelated to $\mathfrak{a}$. Therefore the elements of $I[x, y]$ which are related to $\mathfrak{a}$ are precisely the polynomials with zero constant terms, in other words, the elements of the ideal (x, y).

Before proceeding, it may be pointed out that the set M of all elements of R which are unrelated to $\mathfrak{a}$ is a multiplicative system. For if c and d are unrelated to $\mathfrak{a}$, a congruence

$$cdx \equiv 0(\mathfrak{a})$$

implies that $dx \equiv 0(\mathfrak{a})$ and this, in turn, implies that $x \equiv 0(\mathfrak{a})$. Hence cd is unrelated to $\mathfrak{a}$, and is therefore an element of M.

Since the multiplicative system M does not meet the ideal (0), Lemma 2 of the preceding section asserts the existence of at least one ideal which is maximal in the set of all ideals related to $\mathfrak{a}$, and that each such maximal ideal is necessarily prime. An ideal which is maximal in the set of all ideals related to $\mathfrak{a}$ may be called a *maximal prime ideal belonging to* $\mathfrak{a}$.* Otherwise expressed, an ideal $\mathfrak{p}$ is a maximal prime ideal belonging to $\mathfrak{a}$ if and only if $\mathfrak{p}$ is related to $\mathfrak{a}$ but any ideal $\mathfrak{n}$ such that $\mathfrak{p} \subset \mathfrak{n}$ is unrelated to $\mathfrak{a}$.

---

* In this definition, it is clear that the word *prime* could be omitted, since an ideal with the maximal property in question is necessarily prime. However, the present terminology will be justified in Chapter IX where, for a certain class of ideals, we

We now show that $\mathfrak{a}$ *is contained in every maximal prime ideal* $\mathfrak{p}$ *belonging to* $\mathfrak{a}$. Consider the sum $(\mathfrak{a}, \mathfrak{p})$ of the ideals $\mathfrak{a}$ and $\mathfrak{p}$, and let $a + p$ be any element of this sum, where $a \, \varepsilon \, \mathfrak{a}$, $p \, \varepsilon \, \mathfrak{p}$. Since $\mathfrak{p}$ is related to $\mathfrak{a}$, we have $pr \equiv 0(\mathfrak{a})$ for some r not in $\mathfrak{a}$. Hence $(a + p)r \equiv 0(\mathfrak{a})$, that is, $a + p$ is related to $\mathfrak{a}$. Thus $(\mathfrak{a}, \mathfrak{p})$ is related to $\mathfrak{a}$ and, since $\mathfrak{p} \subseteq (\mathfrak{a}, \mathfrak{p})$, the maximal property of $\mathfrak{p}$ shows that $\mathfrak{p} = (\mathfrak{a}, \mathfrak{p})$. This, however, implies that $\mathfrak{a} \subseteq \mathfrak{p}$, and the desired conclusion is reached.

THEOREM 26. *Every element or ideal which is related to* $\mathfrak{a}$ *is contained in a maximal prime ideal belonging to* $\mathfrak{a}$.

We first observe that if b is related to $\mathfrak{a}$, the ideal (b) is related to $\mathfrak{a}$. For if $br \equiv 0(\mathfrak{a})$, $r \not\equiv 0(\mathfrak{a})$, the product of r by any element of (b) is clearly in $\mathfrak{a}$. Hence, in the proof of the theorem, the only case which need be considered is that of an *ideal* which is related to $\mathfrak{a}$.

If $\mathfrak{b}$ is an ideal related to $\mathfrak{a}$, the multiplicative system M, which consists of the elements of R unrelated to $\mathfrak{a}$, contains no element of $\mathfrak{b}$. Lemma 2 of the preceding section then shows the existence of a maximal prime ideal $\mathfrak{p}$ belonging to $\mathfrak{a}$ such that $\mathfrak{b} \subseteq \mathfrak{p}$.

Let us return to a further consideration of the ideal $\mathfrak{a} = (x^2y, xy^2)$ in the ring $I[x, y]$. It was shown above that the elements of $I[x, y]$ which are related to $\mathfrak{a}$ are the polynomials with zero constant terms, that is, the elements of the prime ideal (x, y). In this case, therefore, (x, y) is the only maximal prime ideal belonging to $\mathfrak{a}$. The minimal prime ideals belonging to $\mathfrak{a}$ are just the ideals (x) and (y), both of which are contained in the maximal prime ideal belonging to $\mathfrak{a}$. This is a simple illustration of a general

---

define a *set of prime ideals belonging to* $\mathfrak{a}$. A maximal (minimal) prime ideal belonging to $\mathfrak{a}$ is then just an ideal which is maximal (minimal) in this set of prime ideals.

result which will presently be proved as Theorem 27. First, however, we may remark that a maximal prime ideal belonging to an ideal need not be a maximal ideal in the ring. The example under discussion furnishes an illustration of this fact. It was pointed out in §20 that the prime ideal (x, y) is contained in the prime ideal $(x, y, 2)$, so that the maximal prime ideal belonging to (x^2y, xy^2) is not a maximal ideal in $I[x, y]$.

Theorem 25 shows that every maximal prime ideal belonging to $\mathfrak{a}$ necessarily contains a minimal prime ideal belonging to $\mathfrak{a}$. We shall now prove

THEOREM 27. *Every minimal prime ideal belonging to* $\mathfrak{a}$ *is contained in a maximal prime ideal belonging to* $\mathfrak{a}$.

This will be established by showing that a minimal prime ideal belonging to $\mathfrak{a}$ is necessarily related to $\mathfrak{a}$, and the desired result will follow from the preceding theorem. Let $\mathfrak{p}$ be a minimal prime ideal belonging to $\mathfrak{a}$, and b any element of R unrelated to $\mathfrak{a}$. We shall show that $b \ \varepsilon \ C(\mathfrak{p})$, and hence that all elements of $\mathfrak{p}$ are related to $\mathfrak{a}$. By Lemma 3 of the preceding section, $C(\mathfrak{p})$ is a maximal multiplicative system which does not meet $\mathfrak{a}$. Let us now consider the multiplicative system M consisting of all elements of any one of the following forms:

$$b^i, \ s, \ b^i s \quad (s \ \varepsilon \ C(\mathfrak{p}), \ i = 1, \ 2, \ \cdots),$$

and show that M does not meet $\mathfrak{a}$. Since $\mathfrak{a} \subseteq \mathfrak{p}$, no element s of $C(\mathfrak{p})$ is in $\mathfrak{a}$. Furthermore $b^i \not\equiv 0(\mathfrak{a})$ since we have shown that the radical of $\mathfrak{a}$ is related to $\mathfrak{a}$, and b is unrelated to $\mathfrak{a}$. Now suppose that, for some positive integer j which we may obviously assume chosen as small as possible, $b^j s \equiv 0(\mathfrak{a})$ for some fixed element s of $C(\mathfrak{p})$. It is clear that $j \neq 1$, as otherwise b would be related to $\mathfrak{a}$. Hence we may write

$$b(b^{j-1}s) \equiv 0(\mathfrak{a}),$$

while $b^{j-1}s \not\equiv 0(\mathfrak{a})$ because of the way in which j was chosen. This, however, shows that b is related to $\mathfrak{a}$, which is a contradiction. Thus M does not meet $\mathfrak{a}$ and, since M contains $C(\mathfrak{p})$, the maximal property of $C(\mathfrak{p})$ implies that $M = C(\mathfrak{p})$. This means that $b \; \varepsilon \; C(\mathfrak{p})$, and the proof is completed.

REFERENCES

Most of the results of this chapter, and other related results, will be found in Krull [2]. See also Krull [3] and Bochner [1]. Prime ideals are briefly discussed in van der Waerden [1], Chapter III; Dubreil [1], Chapter IV (D).

The Maximum Principle is due to Zorn. For expositions of this principle, see Zorn [1] and Tukey [1].

CHAPTER VI

DIRECT AND SUBDIRECT SUMS

25. Direct sum of two rings. Let S_1 and S_2 be any two rings, and consider the set of all symbols (s_1, s_2) where $s_1 \in S_1$, $s_2 \in S_2$. If we define addition and multiplication of these symbols by

$$(s_1, s_2) + (t_1, t_2) = (s_1 + t_1, s_2 + t_2),$$

and

$$(s_1, s_2)(t_1, t_2) = (s_1 t_1, s_2 t_2),$$

it is easy to verify that this set becomes a ring S which we call the *direct sum* of S_1 and S_2, and denote by $S_1 \dotplus S_2$.

Clearly, the zero element of $S = S_1 \dotplus S_2$ is $(0, 0)$, the first 0 being the zero of S_1, the second the zero of S_2. If S_1 and S_2 have unit elements e_1 and e_2 respectively, then S has the unit element (e_1, e_2). If both S_1 and S_2 have more than one element, S has proper divisors of zero since

$$(s_1, 0)(0, s_2) = (0, 0)$$

for every s_1 in S_1, s_2 in S_2. Furthermore, S is a commutative ring if and only if both S_1 and S_2 are commutative. It is also obvious that the one-to-one correspondence

$$(s_1, s_2) \leftrightarrow (s_2, s_1)$$

between elements of $S_1 \dotplus S_2$ and those of $S_2 \dotplus S_1$ is an isomorphism, and we shall therefore not distinguish between these rings.

The set of all elements of S of the form $(s_1, 0)$, where $s_1 \in S_1$, is a subring S_1' (actually an ideal) of S which is isomorphic to S_1 by the correspondence

$$s_1 \leftrightarrow (s_1, 0).$$

In like manner, the set of all elements of S of the form $(0, s_2)$, where $s_2 \ \varepsilon \ S_2$, is a subring S_2' of S isomorphic to S_2. If $s = (s_1, s_2)$ is any element of S, the correspondence

$$s \to (s_1, 0)$$

is a homomorphism of S onto S_1', and the elements of S which correspond to the zero element of S_1' are precisely the elements of S_2'. It follows from the fundamental theorem on homomorphisms that

$$S/S_2' \cong S_1' \cong S_1,$$

and similarly we see that

$$S/S_1' \cong S_2' \cong S_2.$$

Since

$$(s_1, s_2) = (s_1, 0) + (0, s_2),$$

it is clear that every element of S is expressible as a sum of elements of S_1' and S_2' respectively, and moreover in a unique way.*

A principal reason for studying direct sums is that a ring may be isomorphic to a direct sum of rings which are, in some way, of a simpler structure than the given ring. As an illustration, consider the ring I_6 of integers modulo 6, whose elements are $0', 1', 2', 3', 4', 5'$. This ring is certainly not a field since it has proper divisors of zero, but we shall now point out that it is isomorphic to the direct sum $I_2 + I_3$ of the two fields I_2 and I_3. Let us denote the elements of I_2 by $0_2', 1_2'$; and those of I_3 by $0_3',$

---

* For this reason, in the literature S is frequently called the direct sum of its ideals S_1' and S_2'. However, we shall find it convenient to say, in accordance with the definition given above, that S is the direct sum of S_1 and S_2, which are respectively isomorphic to S_1' and S_2'.

$1'_3$, $2'_3$. A straightforward verification will show that the following correspondence between elements of I_6 and those of $I_2 \dotplus I_3$ is actually an isomorphism:

$$0' \leftrightarrow (0'_2 , 0'_3), \qquad 3' \leftrightarrow (1'_2 , 0'_3),$$

$$1' \leftrightarrow (1'_2 , 1'_3), \qquad 4' \leftrightarrow (0'_2 , 1'_3),$$

$$2' \leftrightarrow (0'_2 , 2'_3), \qquad 5' \leftrightarrow (1'_2 , 2'_3).$$

This example also serves to illustrate the next theorem to be established below.

We recall that a ring S has positive characteristic n if $ns = 0$ for all elements s of S, and n is the least positive integer such that this is so.

THEOREM 28. *If a ring S has positive characteristic $n = n_1 n_2$, where n_1 and n_2 are greater than 1 and $(n_1 , n_2) = (1)$, then $S \cong S_2 \dotplus S_1$, where S_i is a ring of characteristic n_i $(i = 1, 2)$.*

We recall from §12 that $(n_1 , n_2) = (1)$ means merely that the integers n_1 and n_2 have 1 as greatest common divisor. It is clear that there exist integers k, l, such that

$$1 = n_1 k + n_2 l,$$

and hence

$$(29) \qquad s = n_1 k s + n_2 l s$$

for every s in S. Let S_2 be the set of all elements of S of the form $n_1 k s$, $s \; \varepsilon \; S$. It follows easily that S_2 is a ring, and its characteristic does not exceed n_2 since $n_2(n_1 k s) = n k s = 0$. In like manner, the set S_1 of all elements of S of the form $n_2 l s$ is a ring whose characteristic does not exceed n_1 .

From (29), we see that

$$n_1 k s = (n_1 k)^2 s + n k l s$$

and, since $ns = 0$, this implies that

$$(n_1 k)^2 s = n_1 k s$$

for every element s of S. Similarly, also

$$(n_2 l)^2 s \ = \ n_2 l s.$$

These relations will be used presently.

We now show that the correspondence

(30) $s \ \rightarrow \ (n_1 k s, \ n_2 l s)$

defines an isomorphism of S with the direct sum $S_2 \dotplus S_1$.
If s and t are arbitrary elements of S, then

$$s + t \rightarrow (n_1 k(s + t), n_2 l(s + t)) = (n_1 k s, n_2 l s) + (n_1 k t, n_2 l t),$$

and the above relations show that also

$$st \ \rightarrow \ (n_1 k s t, \ n_2 l s t) \ = \ ((n_1 k)^2 s t, \ (n_2 l)^2 s t)$$
$$= \ (n_1 k s, \ n_2 l s)(n_1 k t, \ n_2 l t).$$

Furthermore,

$$n_1 k s \ + \ n_2 l t \ \rightarrow \ (n_1 k s, \ n_2 l t),$$

so that every element of $S_2 \dotplus S_1$ is the image of some
element of S. It follows that the correspondence (30) is
a homomorphism of S onto $S_2 \dotplus S_1$. However, if $s \rightarrow$
$(0, 0)$, we see that $n_1 k s = n_2 l s = 0$ and then (29) shows that
$s \ = \ 0$. Thus the homomorphism has zero kernel and is
therefore actually an isomorphism.

To complete the proof of the theorem, we only need to
show that the characteristic of S_i is n_i $(i = 1, 2)$. If S_i
has characteristic m_i, we have already pointed out that
$m_i \leq n_i$. If (s_2 , s_1) is any element cf $S_2 \dotplus S_1$, it follows
that

$$m_1 m_2 (s_2 , s_1) \ = \ (m_1 m_2 s_2 , m_1 m_2 s_1) \ = \ (0, 0),$$

and the characteristic of $S_2 \dotplus S_1$ can not be greater than
$m_1 m_2$. Since n is the characteristic of S it is also the characteristic of the isomorphic ring $S_2 \dotplus S_1$, and thus

$n \leq m_1 m_2$. But $m_i \leq n_i$ implies that $m_1 m_2 \leq n_1 n_2 = n$, and hence we must have $n = n_1 n_2 = m_1 m_2$. Again making use of the fact that $m_i \leq n_i$ $(i = 1, 2)$, we see that $m_i = n_i$, and the proof is therefore completed.

26. Direct sum of any set of rings. The concepts introduced in the preceding section can be readily extended as follows. Let S_i $(i = 1, 2, \cdots)$ be any finite or infinite set of rings, distinct or identical, and consider the set S of all symbols $(s_1, s_2, \cdots)$ where $s_i \, \varepsilon \, S_i$ $(i = 1, 2, \cdots)$. If we make the following natural definitions,

$$(s_1, s_2, \cdots) + (t_1, t_2, \cdots) = (s_1 + t_1, s_2 + t_2, \cdots),$$

$$(s_1, s_2, \cdots)(t_1, t_2, \cdots) = (s_1 t_1, s_2 t_2, \cdots),$$

it is clear that S is a ring which we shall call the *direct sum* of the rings S_i $(i = 1, 2, \cdots)$. It may be pointed out that this notation is a convenient one, but it is not intended to imply that the number of rings S_i is necessarily countable. As a matter of fact, the concept of direct sum does not depend upon the cardinal number of this set of rings, or upon the set being well-ordered. We may also remark that the trivial case in which the set of rings S_i contains only one ring is included in the above definition. This will serve to simplify the statements of certain theorems to be proved later.

Most of the simpler properties of the direct sum of two rings can be easily extended to the direct sum S of any set of rings S_i. The zero element of S is $(0, 0, \cdots)$, the symbol in the ith place being the zero element of S_i. The ring S has a unit element if and only if each ring S_i has a unit element e_i, in which case the unit element of S is $(e_1, e_2, \cdots)$. The set of all elements of the form $(s_1, 0, 0, \cdots)$, where $s_1 \, \varepsilon \, S_1$, is a subring S_1' of S which is isomorphic to S_1. The correspondence

$$(s_1, s_2, s_3, \cdots) \rightarrow (s_1, 0, 0, \cdots)$$

is a homomorphism of S onto S_1', and the kernel $\mathfrak{n}_1$ of this homomorphism consists of all elements of the form

$$(0, s_2, s_3, \cdots) \quad (s_i \, \varepsilon \, S_i \, ; i = 2, 3, \cdots).$$

It follows that $\mathfrak{n}_1$ is isomorphic to the direct sum of the rings S_i $(i = 2, 3, \cdots)$, and that

$$S/\mathfrak{n}_1 \cong S_1' \cong S_1.$$

Obviously, similar remarks hold if S_1 is replaced by any other one of the given rings.

The direct sum of a *finite* number of rings

$$S_i \qquad (i = 1, 2, \cdots, m)$$

may be conveniently denoted by

$$S = S_1 \dotplus S_2 \dotplus \cdots \dotplus S_m.$$

If $\mathfrak{b}_i$ is an ideal in S_i $(i = 1, 2, \cdots, m)$, it is clear that

$$\mathfrak{b}_1 \dotplus \mathfrak{b}_2 \dotplus \cdots \dotplus \mathfrak{b}_m$$

is an ideal in S. Conversely, suppose that $\mathfrak{a}$ is an ideal in S. We shall now show that *if S_i has a unit element $e_i (i = 1, 2, \cdots, m)$, then*

$$\mathfrak{a} = \mathfrak{a}_1 \dotplus \mathfrak{a}_2 \dotplus \cdots \dotplus \mathfrak{a}_m,$$

where $\mathfrak{a}_i$ is an ideal in S_i $(i = 1, 2, \cdots, m)$. Under the homomorphism

$$(s_1, s_2, \cdots, s_m) \to s_i$$

of S onto S_i, let $\mathfrak{a}_i$ be the image of $\mathfrak{a}$, that is, $\mathfrak{a}_i$ consists of all elements of S_i which are images of elements of $\mathfrak{a}$. It follows that $\mathfrak{a}_i$ is an ideal in S_i. For simplicity of notation, let us consider the ideal $\mathfrak{a}_1$ in S_1. If b_1 is any element of $\mathfrak{a}_1$, there exists an element of $\mathfrak{a}$ with b_1 in the first position, say $(b_1, b_2, \cdots, b_m)$. It follows that

$$(b_1, b_2, \cdots, b_m)(e_1, 0, \cdots, 0) = (b_1, 0, \cdots, 0) \, \varepsilon \, \mathfrak{a},$$

and thus $\mathfrak{a}$ contains *all* elements of S of the form $(b_1, 0, \cdots, 0)$, $b_1 \; \varepsilon \; \mathfrak{a}_1$. In like manner, $\mathfrak{a}$ contains all elements of the form $(0, b_2, 0, \cdots, 0)$, $b_2 \; \varepsilon \; \mathfrak{a}_2$, and so on. Finally, then, $\mathfrak{a}$ contains all sums of these elements, that is, $\mathfrak{a}$ contains $\mathfrak{a}_1 \dotplus \mathfrak{a}_2 \dotplus \cdots \dotplus \mathfrak{a}_m$. However, in view of the definition of the $\mathfrak{a}_i$, every element of $\mathfrak{a}$ is contained in this direct sum, and hence

$$\mathfrak{a} = \mathfrak{a}_1 \dotplus \mathfrak{a}_2 \dotplus \cdots \dotplus \mathfrak{a}_m,$$

as we wished to show. This result will be used in §28.

It is readily seen that if $S \cong S_1 \dotplus S_2$ and $S_2 \cong S_2' \dotplus S_2''$, then

$$S \cong S_1 \dotplus S_2' \dotplus S_2''$$

This fact may be used to extend Theorem 28 as follows:

THEOREM 29. *If S has characteristic*

$$n = p_1^{k_1} p_2^{k_2} \cdots p_m^{k_m},$$

where the p_i are distinct primes and each $k_i \geq 1$, then

$$S \cong S_1 \dotplus S_2 \dotplus \cdots \dotplus S_m,$$

where S_i has characteristic $p_i^{k_i}$ ($i = 1, 2, \cdots, m$).

The proof is almost obvious. If we set $n_1 = p_1^{k_1}$, $n_2 = p_2^{k_2} \cdots p_m^{k_m}$, then $(n_1, n_2) = (1)$ and, by Theorem 28, $S \cong S_1 \dotplus T_1$, where S_1 has characteristic n_1 and T_1 has characteristic n_2. If $m > 2$, by the same argument applied to T_1, $T_1 \cong S_2 \dotplus T_2$, where S_2 has characteristic $p_2^{k_2}$ and T_2 has characteristic $p_3^{k_3} \cdots p_m^{k_m}$. The remark preceding the statement of the theorem then shows that $S \cong S_1 \dotplus S_2 \dotplus T_2$, and a repetition of this argument clearly leads to the desired result.

27. Subrings of direct sums and subdirect sums. It may well happen that a ring is isomorphic to a *subring* of a

direct sum of rings of some certain kind, but not to a direct sum of such rings. We therefore proceed to a study of subrings of direct sums.

As an illustration of the next concept to be introduced, let us consider the direct sum of the two rings I_2 and I_4. If we denote the elements of I_2 by $0_2'$, $1_2'$, and those of I_4 by $0_4'$, $1_4'$, $2_4'$, $3_4'$, it may be easily verified that the set T_1 consisting of the elements $(0_2', 0_4')$, $(1_2', 1_4')$, $(0_2', 2_4')$, and $(1_2', 3_4')$ is a subring of this direct sum. Since every element of I_2 and also every element of I_4 is actually used in writing down the elements of T_1, we say that T_1 is a *subdirect sum* of the rings I_2 and I_4 in accordance with a general definition to be given presently. On the other hand, the subring T_2 of the direct sum of I_2 and I_4 which consists of the elements $(0_2', 0_4')$, $(0_2', 2_4')$, $(1_2', 0_4')$, and $(1_2', 2_4')$ is not a subdirect sum of these rings since the elements $1_4'$ and $3_4'$ are not used.

Now let S be the direct sum of an arbitrary set of rings S_i, the elements of S being denoted by

$$s = (s_1, s_2, \cdots) \qquad (s_i \, \varepsilon \, S_i).$$

If T is a subring of S, and $t = (t_1, t_2, \cdots) \, \varepsilon \, T$, the correspondence

$$t \rightarrow t_i$$

defines a homomorphism of T *into* S_i and therefore *onto* a subring S_i' of S_i. If, for every i, $S_i' = S_i$, we shall say that T is a *subdirect sum* of the rings S_i. Thus if T is any subring of the direct sum of rings S_i, it is a subdirect sum of certain rings S_i', where $S_i' \subseteq S_i$. Also, if T is a subdirect sum of the S_i it is clearly a subring of the direct sum of rings S_i^*, where S_i^* is *any* ring containing S_i.

It should perhaps be remarked that the direct sum of a set of rings S_i is uniquely determined (up to an isomorphism) by the rings S_i. However, there may well exist many different subdirect sums of a given set of rings.

Let T be a subdirect sum of the rings S_i, and R a ring which is isomorphic to T by the correspondence $r \leftrightarrow t$. Thus the correspondence

$$r \leftrightarrow t \rightarrow t_i$$

defines a homomorphism of R *onto* S_i. Let us denote this homomorphism by g_i, and write $g_i(r) = t_i$ $(i = 1, 2, \cdots)$. If r is not the zero element of R, then t can not be the zero element $(0, 0, \cdots)$ of T; thus, for some i, $g_i(r) \neq 0$. This establishes one part of the following theorem:

THEOREM 30. *A ring R is isomorphic to a subdirect sum of rings S_i if and only if there exists a homomorphism h_i of R onto S_i $(i = 1, 2, \cdots)$ such that for every nonzero element r of R, $h_i(r) \neq 0$ for at least one i.*

To complete the proof of the theorem, we now assume the existence of such a set of homomorphisms. Since $h_i(r) \; \varepsilon \; S_i$, the correspondence

(31) $$r \rightarrow (h_1(r), h_2(r), \cdots)$$

is a correspondence of R *into* the direct sum S of the rings S_i. Furthermore, since h_i is a homomorphism, we have

$$h_i(r + r') = h_i(r) + h_i(r'),$$

and

$$h_i(rr') = h_i(r)h_i(r').$$

Thus the correspondence (31) is such that

$$r + r' \rightarrow (h_1(r + r'), h_2(r + r'), \cdots)$$
$$= (h_1(r), h_2(r), \cdots) + (h_1(r'), h_2(r'), \cdots),$$

and

$$rr' \rightarrow (h_1(rr'), h_2(rr'), \cdots)$$
$$= (h_1(r), h_2(r), \cdots)(h_1(r'), h_2(r'), \cdots);$$

hence is a homomorphism of R into S. However, since h_i is given as a homomorphism of R *onto* S_i, the correspondence (31) is actually a homomorphism of R onto a subdirect sum of the rings S_i. Furthermore, the fact that for nonzero r, $h_i(r) \neq 0$ for some i shows that this homomorphism has zero kernel and hence is an isomorphism.

COROLLARY. *If $\{a_i\}$ is a set of ideals in R having zero intersection, then R is isomorphic to a subdirect sum of the residue class rings R/a_i.*

If we make the element r of R correspond to the residue class to which r belongs modulo a_i, this defines a homomorphism h_i of R onto R/a_i. Furthermore, if $r \neq 0$, r is not in all the ideals a_i since these ideals have zero intersection. Hence, for some i, $h_i(r) \neq 0$, and the preceding theorem is then applicable.

We now apply this corollary to establish the following theorem:

THEOREM 31. *For a commutative ring R, the following conditions are equivalent:*

(i) *R is isomorphic to a subdirect sum of integral domains.*

(ii) *R is isomorphic to a subring of a direct sum of fields.*

(iii) *R has no nonzero nilpotent element.*

Since, by Corollary 1 to Theorem 23, an integral domain can be imbedded in a field, it is clear that (i) implies (ii). If

$$r = (r_1, r_2, \cdots)$$

is any element of a direct sum of fields, then

$$r^n = (r_1^n, r_2^n, \cdots),$$

and $r^n = 0$ only if each $r_i^n = 0$. However, since r_i is an element of a field, $r_i^n = 0$ implies that $r_i = 0$. Thus a direct sum of fields can contain no nonzero nilpotent element, and this shows that (ii) implies (iii).

The proof will be completed by showing that (iii) implies (i). Let R be a commutative ring without nonzero nilpotent elements. In the language of the preceding chapter, this means that the radical of the ideal (0) is (0). Hence, by Theorem 24, there exists in R a set of prime ideals $\{\mathfrak{p}_i\}$ having zero intersection, and the Corollary to Theorem 30 then states that R is isomorphic to a subdirect sum of the rings $R/\mathfrak{p}_i$. Since each $\mathfrak{p}_i$ is a prime ideal, $R/\mathfrak{p}_i$ is an integral domain, and hence (i) is true.

This theorem characterizes the rings which are isomorphic to a *subring* of a direct sum of fields. In §30 we shall obtain a characterization of those rings which are isomorphic to a *subdirect* sum of fields.

If R is a commutative ring, the radical of the zero ideal is frequently called the *radical of the ring R*; in other words, the radical of R consists of all nilpotent elements of R. Theorem 31 thus characterizes a ring which is isomorphic to a subdirect sum of integral domains as a ring of zero radical.

COROLLARY. *If $\mathfrak{r}$ is the radical of the commutative ring R, then $R/\mathfrak{r}$ is isomorphic to a subdirect sum of integral domains.*

This follows at once from the preceding theorem and the observation of §21 that if $\mathfrak{r}$ is the radical of *any* ideal in R, then $R/\mathfrak{r}$ has no nonzero nilpotent elements.

28. A finite case. In order to avoid possible confusion, we shall sometimes find it convenient to call the direct sum of rings S_i, as previously defined, the *complete direct sum* of these rings. This term will be used only when it is desired to emphasize that we are referring to a direct sum and not to a subring of a direct sum, or to a subdirect sum.

It was shown above that I_6 is not just isomorphic to a subring of a direct sum of fields but actually to the complete direct sum of the fields I_2 and I_3. On the other hand, Theorem 31 shows that the ring I is isomorphic to a subring of a direct sum of fields, but since it has no proper divisors of zero it can not be isomorphic to a complete direct sum of fields. The purpose of this section is to prove the following theorem which will help to clarify this situation:

THEOREM 32. *A commutative ring R with more than one element is isomorphic to a complete direct sum of a finite number of fields if and only if it has zero radical and contains only a finite number of ideals.*

As a first step in the proof we establish the following

LEMMA. *An integral domain S with more than one element and only a finite number of ideals is a field.*

Let s be a nonzero element, and t an arbitrary element of S. We shall show that there exists an element x of S such that $sx = t$. For each positive integer i, let us denote by $\mathfrak{s}_i$ the ideal in S consisting of all elements of the form ys^i, $y \in S$. Since S has only a finite number of different ideals, for certain positive integers m, n we must have $\mathfrak{s}_m = \mathfrak{s}_n$ with $m < n$. Hence, in particular, ts^m, being an element of $\mathfrak{s}_m$, is also in $\mathfrak{s}_n$, that is, there exists an element z of S such that

$$ts^m = zs^n.$$

Since an integral domain has no proper divisors of zero, it follows that

$$t = zs^{n-m}.$$

If $n - m = 1$, we set $x = z$; while if $n - m > 1$, we set $x = zs^{n-m-1}$. Hence, in either case, there exists an element x of S such that $sx = t$, and S is therefore a field.

We now return to the proof of the theorem, and assume that R has zero radical and only a finite number of ideals. If R has no proper divisors of zero, the lemma shows that R is itself a field and the conclusion of the theorem is immediate. Hence we assume that R has proper divisors of zero, in other words, that (0) is not a prime ideal in R. As in the proof of Theorem 31, there exists a set of prime ideals in R having zero intersection. Furthermore, since this set is necessarily finite, we may assume that *if any one of these prime ideals is omitted, the intersection of the others is different from zero* since, if this is not the case, we may obtain a set with this property by simply omitting certain of the ideals. We thus obtain a set of prime ideals $\mathfrak{p}_j$ $(j = 1, 2, \cdots, k)$ of zero intersection, no one of which is (0) or R, with the property that if $\mathfrak{p}_i$ is any ideal of this set, there is an element of R which is not in $\mathfrak{p}_i$ but is in all $\mathfrak{p}_j$ for $j \neq i$. We shall presently make use of this fact.

Since $\mathfrak{p}_i \neq R$ and is a prime ideal, $R/\mathfrak{p}_i$ is an integral domain with more than one element. Furthermore, under the usual homomorphism $a \rightarrow \bar{a}$ of R onto $R/\mathfrak{p}_i$, different ideals in $R/\mathfrak{p}_i$ have different inverse images in R. Since R has only a finite number of ideals, the same is therefore true of $R/\mathfrak{p}_i$, and the lemma shows that $R/\mathfrak{p}_i$ is a field.

By the proof of the Corollary to Theorem 30, the correspondence

$$(32) \qquad r \leftrightarrow (\bar{r}_1, \bar{r}_2, \cdots, \bar{r}_k)$$

defines an isomorphism of R with a subdirect sum of the fields $R/\mathfrak{p}_i$, $\bar{r}_i$ being the residue class to which r belongs modulo $\mathfrak{p}_i$. We now show that by this correspondence *every* element of the direct sum of the fields $R/\mathfrak{p}_i$ appears as the image of an element of R, and hence that R is isomorphic to the complete direct sum of these fields. Let

$$(\bar{a}_1, \bar{a}_2, \cdots, \bar{a}_k)$$

be any element of this direct sum, and let b_i be an element of R which is not in $\mathfrak{p}_i$ but is in all $\mathfrak{p}_j$ for $j \neq i$. Such an element exists as pointed out above. Then $\bar{b}_i \neq 0$ and, since $R/\mathfrak{p}_i$ is a field, there is an element $\bar{x}_i$ of $R/\mathfrak{p}_i$ such that $\bar{b}_i \bar{x}_i = \bar{a}_i$. Furthermore, by the correspondence (32), b_i corresponds to an element with $\bar{b}_i$ in the i-th place and zeros elsewhere. If then x_i is any element of R in the residue class $\bar{x}_i$ modulo $\mathfrak{p}_i$, we see that

$$b_1 x_1 + b_2 x_2 + \cdots + b_k x_k \leftrightarrow (\bar{a}_1, \bar{a}_2, \cdots, \bar{a}_k).$$

It follows that R is isomorphic to the complete direct sum of the fields $R/\mathfrak{p}_i$.

To prove the other part of the theorem, suppose that R is isomorphic to the complete direct sum of a finite number of fields F_i ($i = 1, 2, \cdots, k$). Clearly, R has no nonzero nilpotent element, that is, R has zero radical; and there remains only to show that R has only a finite number of ideals. This follows almost at once from a result of §26 which states that every ideal in

$$F_1 \dotplus F_2 \dotplus \cdots \dotplus F_k$$

is of the form

$$\mathfrak{a}_1 \dotplus \mathfrak{a}_2 \dotplus \cdots \dotplus \mathfrak{a}_k,$$

where $\mathfrak{a}_i$ is an ideal in F_i. Since the only ideals in the field F_i are (0) and F_i, it is clear that the number of ideals is finite—in fact, 2^k in number. Hence the isomorphic ring R has only a finite number of ideals, and the proof of the theorem is completed.

29. Subdirectly irreducible rings. As in §27, we let T be a subdirect sum of rings S_i, and R a ring which is isomorphic to T by a correspondence $r \leftrightarrow t$. We may say that T is a *representation* of R as a subdirect sum of the rings S_i. If elements of T are denoted by

$$t = (t_1, t_2, \cdots) \qquad (t_i \; \varepsilon \; S_i),$$

then the correspondence

$$(33) \qquad\qquad r \leftrightarrow t \rightarrow t_i$$

defines a homomorphism of R onto S_i $(i = 1, 2, \cdots)$.

It may happen, of course, that some or all of the homomorphisms (33) are actually isomorphisms. As an extreme case, it is clear that under the correspondence

$$r \leftrightarrow (r, r, \cdots),$$

a ring R is isomorphic to a subdirect sum of any number of rings, each identical with R. In this case, every homomorphism (33) is an isomorphism.

A ring R is said to be *subdirectly reducible* if there exists a representation of R as a subdirect sum of rings S_i such that no one of the homomorphisms (33) is an isomorphism. Otherwise, R is *subdirectly irreducible*.

As a simple example, suppose that R is a field. Now a homomorphic image of a field is either a field isomorphic to the given field, or a one-element ring. If the field R is isomorphic to a subdirect sum of rings S_i, not every S_i can be a one-element ring, and hence the homomorphism (33) must be an isomorphism for at least one i. This shows that a field is subdirectly irreducible.

THEOREM 33. *A ring R is subdirectly irreducible if and only if the intersection of all nonzero ideals in R is a nonzero ideal.*

A logically equivalent formulation of this theorem is the following:

THEOREM 33'. *A ring R is subdirectly reducible if and only if there exists in R a set of nonzero ideals with zero intersection.*

We shall prove Theorem 33'. First, suppose that there exists in R a set of nonzero ideals $\mathfrak{a}_i$ with zero intersection. Then the Corollary to Theorem 30 states that R is isomorphic to a subdirect sum T of the rings $R/\mathfrak{a}_i$. Furthermore, the construction used in the proof of the Corollary shows that in this case the homomorphism $r \to t_i$ defined by (33) is actually the usual homomorphism of R onto $R/\mathfrak{a}_i$, that is, t_i is the residue class to which r belongs modulo $\mathfrak{a}_i$. Since all $\mathfrak{a}_i$ are different from zero, no one of the homomorphisms (33) can be an isomorphism, and hence R is subdirectly reducible.

Suppose now that R is subdirectly reducible and therefore R is isomorphic to a subdirect sum T of rings S_i, such that the homomorphism (33) of R onto S_i is not an isomorphism for any i. If $\mathfrak{b}_i$ is the kernel of this homomorphism, then, for each i, $\mathfrak{b}_i \neq (0)$. Furthermore, if $r \neq 0$, this means that some $t_i \neq 0$, so that the nonzero ideals $\mathfrak{b}_i$ have zero intersection.

The significance of the concept of subdirect irreducibility is to be found in the following theorem:

THEOREM 34. *Every ring is isomorphic to a subdirect sum of subdirectly irreducible rings.*

If a is any nonzero element of the arbitrary ring R, consider the class $\mathfrak{A}$ of all ideals in R which do not contain the element a. The class $\mathfrak{A}$ has at least one element since it contains the zero ideal of R. The union of each linear subsystem of $\mathfrak{A}$ is an ideal which does not contain a, and thus is an element of $\mathfrak{A}$. Hence the Maximum Principle asserts the existence of a maximal element of $\mathfrak{A}$; that is, an ideal $\mathfrak{m}_a$ not containing a, but such that if $\mathfrak{m}_a \subset \mathfrak{n}$, then $\mathfrak{n}$ contains a. Furthermore, the intersection of all ideals $\mathfrak{m}_a$, where a varies over the nonzero elements of R, is zero. Hence, by the Corollary to Theorem 30, R is isomorphic to a subdirect sum of the rings $R/\mathfrak{m}_a$. We shall complete the proof by showing that each ring $R/\mathfrak{m}_a$ is subdirectly irreducible.

If, in the usual notation, $\bar{x}$ denotes the residue class to which x belongs modulo $\mathfrak{m}_a$, then clearly $\bar{a} \neq 0$. Let $\mathfrak{f}$ be any nonzero ideal in $R/\mathfrak{m}_a$. Then the set of all elements r of R such that $\bar{r} \, \varepsilon \, \mathfrak{f}$ (the inverse image of $\mathfrak{f}$ under the homomorphism $x \to \bar{x}$) is an ideal $\mathfrak{n}$ in R which contains $\mathfrak{m}_a$. Since $\mathfrak{f} \neq 0$, $\mathfrak{n} \supset \mathfrak{m}_a$, and therefore by the maximal property of $\mathfrak{m}_a$, $\mathfrak{n}$ contains a. It follows that $\mathfrak{f}$ contains $\bar{a}$, that is, every nonzero ideal in $R/\mathfrak{m}_a$ contains $\bar{a}$. Theorem 33 then shows that $R/\mathfrak{m}_a$ is subdirectly irreducible.

In view of this theorem, it becomes of interest to investigate the subdirectly irreducible rings. We have already pointed out that all fields are subdirectly irreducible. However, not all subdirectly irreducible commutative rings are fields, as can be seen by a consideration of the ring I_8. In this ring, every nonzero ideal contains the element $4'$ and thus I_8 is subdirectly irreducible, and it is not a field since it has proper divisors of zero. As a matter of fact, it may be shown that the ring I_{p^k}, where p is a prime, is subdirectly irreducible; it is, however, a field if and only if $k = 1$. It is possible to give a complete, and fairly simple, characterization of the subdirectly irreducible *commutative* rings, but we shall limit ourselves to a proof of the following important result:

THEOREM 35. *A subdirectly irreducible commutative ring R with more than one element and with zero radical is a field.*

By Theorem 33, there is a nonzero element j of R which

is contained in *all* nonzero ideals in R. The ideal consisting of all elements of the form yj^2, $y \, \varepsilon \, R$, contains j^3 which is different from zero since R contains no nonzero nilpotent elements. Thus, this ideal contains j, that is, there is an element x of R such that $xj^2 = j$. If we set $e = xj$, then

$$e^2 = x^2j^2 = x(xj^2) = xj = e,$$

and also $e \neq 0$ since $ej = j \neq 0$. Furthermore, an ideal which contains j must also contain e; hence e is contained in all nonzero ideals.

The set of all elements of R of the form

$$t - te \qquad\qquad (t \, \varepsilon \, R)$$

is an ideal $\mathfrak{a}$. If $\mathfrak{a} \neq (0)$, then $e \, \varepsilon \, \mathfrak{a}$, and we have

$$e = t_1 - t_1e$$

for proper choice of t_1 in R. Since $e^2 = e$, multiplication of this equation by e shows that $e = 0$, which is a contradiction. Therefore $\mathfrak{a} = (0)$, which merely states that $t = te$ for every element t of R; hence e is the unit element of R. Since every nonzero ideal contains e, it follows that R itself is the only nonzero ideal in R.

Now if a is any nonzero element of R, the ideal of elements ax, $x \, \varepsilon \, R$, is a nonzero ideal since it contains $a^2 \neq 0$, and therefore is R. Hence the equation $ax = b$ has a solution for every b in R. This shows that R is a field, and completes the proof of the theorem.

We may point out that the representation of a ring as a subdirect sum of subdirectly irreducible rings is in no sense unique. For example, in the ring I of integers, no nonzero integer is divisible by all primes, and thus the intersection of all prime ideals (p), where p is a prime, is zero. This implies that I is isomorphic to a subdirect sum of the fields $I/(p)$. Similarly, I is also isomorphic to a subdirect sum of the rings $I/(p^2)$, each of which is subdirectly irreducible and no one of which is a field. As a matter of fact, in place of all primes p one may just as well use any infinite set of primes.

30. The Jacobson radical and subdirect sums of fields. The primary purpose of this section is to characterize those rings which have a representation as a subdirect sum of fields. First, however, we introduce some important preliminary concepts.

We recall that the radical of a *commutative* ring has been defined as the ideal consisting of all nilpotent elements. We shall presently define the *Jacobson radical* of a general ring which may well differ from the radical in case the ring is commutative. Actually, for commutative rings, the Jacobson radical bears the same relation to subdirect sums of fields that the previously defined radical does to the *subrings* of direct sums of fields (cf. Theorems 31 and 38).

Let R be an arbitrary ring, not necessarily commutative. An element r of R is said to be *quasi-regular* if there exists in R an element r' such that

$$(34) \qquad r + r' + rr' = 0.$$

If R has a unit element 1, this is equivalent to the condition that

$$(1 + r)(1 + r') = 1.$$

Clearly 0 is quasi-regular, and if R contains more than one element and has a unit element 1, -1 can not be quasi-regular. Furthermore, if $r^n = 0$, then (34) is satisfied by $r' = \sum_{i=1}^{n-1} (-r)^i$, so that every nilpotent element is quasi-regular.

THEOREM 36. *The set $\mathfrak{y}$ of all elements r such that rx is*

quasi-regular for all x in R, is an ideal—the Jacobson radical
of R.

If $r \, \varepsilon \, \mathfrak{y}$, and x and y are arbitrary elements of R, then
rxy is quasi-regular. That is, R contains an element r'
such that

$$rxy + r' + rxyr' = 0.$$

This shows that $rx \, \varepsilon \, \mathfrak{y}$. Furthermore, since

$$yrx + (-yrx - yr'rx) + yrx(-yrx - yr'rx)$$
$$= -y(r' + rxy + rxyr')rx = 0,$$

it follows that $yr \, \varepsilon \, \mathfrak{y}$. There remains only to show that if
$r_1 \, \varepsilon \, \mathfrak{y}$, $r_2 \, \varepsilon \, \mathfrak{y}$, then $r_1 - r_2 \, \varepsilon \, \mathfrak{y}$, that is, that $(r_1 - r_2)x$ is
quasi-regular for each x in R. Since $r_1 \, \varepsilon \, \mathfrak{y}$, there exists an
element r_1' such that

$$r_1 x + r_1' + r_1 x r_1' = 0.$$

Now $r_2(-x - xr_1')$ is quasi-regular since $r_2 \, \varepsilon \, \mathfrak{y}$; hence there
is an element w' such that

$$r_2(-x - xr_1') + w' + r_2(-x - xr_1')w' = 0.$$

It follows that

$$[(r_1 - r_2)x] + (r_1' + w' + r_1'w')$$
$$+ [(r_1 - r_2)x](r_1' + w' + r_1'w') = [r_1 x + r_1' + r_1 x r_1']$$
$$+ [r_2(-x - xr_1') + w' + r_2(-x - xr_1')w']$$
$$+ [r_1 x + r_1' + r_1 x r_1']w' = 0,$$

by the two preceding equations. This shows, however, that
$(r_1 - r_2)x$ is quasi-regular, and the theorem is established.

It may be pointed out that Jacobson *defines* the radical
somewhat differently but shows that his definition is
equivalent to that given above.

If R has a unit element and $r \; \varepsilon \; \mathfrak{y}$, then it is clear that r itself is quasi-regular. As a matter of fact, this is true without the assumption of a unit element as can be seen by the following calculation. Since rx is quasi-regular for every x, we see that $-r^2$ must be quasi-regular, that is, there exists an element s such that

$$-r^2 + s - r^2 s = 0.$$

Hence

$$r + (-r + s - rs) + r(-r + s - rs) = 0,$$

and therefore r is quasi-regular.

We shall now prove

THEOREM 37. *If $\mathfrak{y}$ is the Jacobson radical of R, then $R/\mathfrak{y}$ has zero Jacobson radical.*

Let $\bar{r}$ be an arbitrary element of the Jacobson radical of $R/\mathfrak{y}$, and x any element of R. Then $\bar{r}\bar{x}$ is quasi-regular and hence there is an element $\bar{s}$ of $R/\mathfrak{y}$ such that

$$\bar{r}\bar{x} + \bar{s} + \bar{r}\bar{x}\bar{s} = 0,$$

which implies that

$$rx + s + rxs \equiv 0(\mathfrak{y}).$$

However, elements of $\mathfrak{y}$ are quasi-regular, and hence there is an element t of R such that

$$(rx + s + rxs) + t + (rx + s + rxs)t = 0.$$

From this we see that

$$rx + (s + t + st) + rx(s + t + st) = 0,$$

and rx is quasi-regular. Since this is true for every x, r is in $\mathfrak{y}$ and hence $\bar{r} = 0$.

Although the Jacobson radical has important applications in the study of general rings, we now restrict attention to commutative rings and shall prove the following theorem:

THEOREM 38. *A commutative ring R with more than one element is isomorphic to a subdirect sum of fields if and only if the Jacobson radical η of R is zero.*

First, suppose that $\eta = (0)$. If r is any nonzero element of R there therefore exists an element s of R such that rs is not quasi-regular. Let us denote by $\mathfrak{a}$ the set of elements of R of the form $x + rsx$, $x \,\varepsilon\, R$. Then $\mathfrak{a}$ is an ideal in R which does not contain rs. For if $rs \,\varepsilon\, \mathfrak{a}$, then for some element y of R,

$$y + rsy = rs,$$

which is equivalent to

$$rs + (-y) + rs(-y) = 0.$$

This, however, is impossible since rs is not quasi-regular, and hence $\mathfrak{a}$ does not contain rs. As in previous applications of the Maximum Principle, it follows that in the set of all ideals containing $\mathfrak{a}$ but not containing rs, there exists a maximal one, say $\mathfrak{m}$. Now $\mathfrak{m}$ is actually a maximal ideal in R for if $\mathfrak{m} \subset \mathfrak{n}$, then $\mathfrak{n}$ contains $\mathfrak{a}$ and rs; hence if x is any element of R, $\mathfrak{n}$ must contain $(x + rsx) - rsx = x$.

We now show that $R/\mathfrak{m}$ is a field. By Theorem 19, it is only necessary to prove that $d \not\equiv 0(\mathfrak{m})$ implies that $d^2 \not\equiv 0(\mathfrak{m})$. Suppose, then, that $d \not\equiv 0(\mathfrak{m})$. Since $d + rsd \equiv 0(\mathfrak{a})$ and $\mathfrak{a} \subseteq \mathfrak{m}$, it follows that $rsd \not\equiv 0(\mathfrak{m})$. Now $(d, \mathfrak{m}) = R$ since $\mathfrak{m}$ is a maximal ideal in R. Thus, in particular,

$$rs = td + id + m_1,$$

for suitable choice of t in R, i in I, m_1 in $\mathfrak{m}$. Hence

$$rsd \equiv td^2 + id^2(\mathfrak{m}).$$

It follows that $d^2 \not\equiv 0(\mathfrak{m})$, as otherwise we would have $rsd \equiv 0(\mathfrak{m})$, a contradiction.

We have now shown that given any nonzero element r of R there exists an ideal $\mathfrak{m}$ in R not containing rs and therefore not containing r, such that $R/\mathfrak{m}$ is a field. The intersection of all such ideals $\mathfrak{m}$ is clearly zero, and the Corollary to Theorem 30 shows that R is isomorphic to a subdirect sum of the fields $R/\mathfrak{m}$.

Conversely, let R be isomorphic to a subdirect sum of fields F_i under the correspondence

$$r \leftrightarrow (r_1, r_2, \cdots).$$

If a is any nonzero element of R, not all a_i can be zero and, for convenience, let us assume that $a_1 \neq 0$. Let x_1 be an element of F_1 such that $a_1 x_1 = -e_1$, where e_1 is the unit element of F_1, and x an element of R such that $x \rightarrow x_1$ under the homomorphism $r \rightarrow r_1$ of R onto F_1. Thus, under this homomorphism, the image of ax is $-e_1$ which can not be quasi-regular. Since the homomorphic image of a quasi-regular element is necessarily quasi-regular, it follows that ax is not quasi-regular, and hence that a is not in $\mathfrak{y}$. Since a is any nonzero element of R, this means that $\mathfrak{y} = (0)$, as we wished to show.

In view of Theorem 37 we have at once the following

COROLLARY. *If $\mathfrak{y}$ is the Jacobson radical of the commutative ring R and $\mathfrak{y} \neq R$, then $R/\mathfrak{y}$ is isomorphic to a subdirect sum of fields.*

It may be of interest to discuss briefly the relation between Theorems 31 and 38. If a is a nilpotent element of a *commutative* ring R, then ax is nilpotent for all x. Since a nilpotent element is quasi-regular, it follows that $\mathfrak{y}$ contains all nilpotent elements, that is, the Jacobson radical contains the radical. However, $\mathfrak{y}$ may contain elements which are not nilpotent, and hence there exist rings which are isomorphic to a subring of a direct sum of fields but not to a subdirect sum of fields. As a simple example, let S be the ring of those rational numbers of the form i/m, where i is an arbitrary integer and m is an *odd* integer (see §19). Now elements $2x$ are of the form $2i/m$, and the equation

$$\frac{2i}{m} + \frac{(-2i)}{2i + m} + \frac{2i(-2i)}{m(2i + m)} = 0$$

shows that every element $2x$ is quasi-regular. As a matter of fact, it is easily verified that no other elements are quasi-regular, and hence $\mathfrak{y} = (2)$. However, S can have no nonzero nilpotent element since it is a subring of the field of rational numbers.

REFERENCES

The concept of direct sum of a finite number of rings occurs in almost all the standard texts on abstract algebra. Early references to the direct sum of an infinite set of rings are Krull [2], Köthe [1], and Stone [1]. See McCoy [6] for an exposition of known results on subdirect sums of rings, and complete references.

For the material of §27, and related results, see McCoy and Montgomery [1] and McCoy [1].

Subdirectly irreducible rings were first introduced in Birkhoff [1]. A characterization of the subdirectly irreducible commutative rings will be found in McCoy [5].

Our discussion of subdirect sums of fields is based on Jacobson [2]. Actually, Jacobson obtains a result for general rings which reduces to our Theorem 38 in case the rings happen to be commutative. Still another definition of radical, related to that of Jacobson, is given in Brown and McCoy [2].

Chapter VII

BOOLEAN RINGS AND SOME GENERALIZATIONS

31. Algebra of logic and algebra of classes. The so-called "algebra of logic" had its origin in the fundamental work of the English mathematician and logician, George Boole (1815–1864), and is therefore usually called *Boolean algebra*. Although there is a very extensive literature on this subject, we shall present just enough to furnish a partial setting for the material of the next section.

Let us consider a set of "statements" which may be either true or false. For concreteness, we shall consider the class $\mathcal{C}$ of all books in the Library of Congress, and statements about any book x of $\mathcal{C}$. As examples, we may use the following statements:

(α): x has exactly 300 pages,

(β): x was published in 1929,

(γ): x is printed in the French language,

(δ): The date of accession of x was 50 B.C.,

(ϵ): x has at least one page.

It will be noted that (δ) is true for no book, and (ϵ) for all books of $\mathcal{C}$.

From a given set of statements, such as those listed above, it is possible to construct others by use of the familiar connectives "and," "or," and "not." (The word "or" is used in the ordinary sense of either $\cdots$ or $\cdots$ or both.) Thus, we may get compound statements of the following types: —(α) *and* (β): x has exactly 300 pages and was published in 1929; (α) *or* (β): x has exactly 300 pages or was published in 1929; *not* (α): x does not have exactly 300 pages.

In any extended study of this subject, it is convenient and suggestive to introduce appropriate symbols for "and," "or," and "not;" in fact, this was one of the great contributions of Boole. However, we shall not do this but instead make the following convenient shift of emphasis.

Let any statement (α) correspond to the class (or set) a of books of $\mathcal{C}$ for which statement (α) is true, and indicate the correspondence by $(\alpha) \rightarrow a$. Thus statement (α) merely asserts that x is a member of the class a. In this notation, it will be observed that $(\delta) \rightarrow d$, where d is the void class, while $(\epsilon) \rightarrow e$, which is the entire class $\mathcal{C}$. Each of our original statements, and also each of the compound ones we can construct as above, thus corresponds to a subclass of $\mathcal{C}$, the void class and the entire class $\mathcal{C}$ being included. The "algebra of statements" is thus equivalent to an "algebra of subclasses" of the class $\mathcal{C}$.

It is convenient to make use of a notation which was introduced in Example 2 of §2. By the *product ab* of two subclasses we shall mean the intersection of a and b. The *sum $a + b$* is the class of elements of $\mathcal{C}$ which are in a or in b *but not in both*. It may now be verified that the union of a and b, that is, the set of elements in a or in b, is just $(a + b) + ab$, while $a + e$ is the set of elements of $\mathcal{C}$ which are not in a, in other words, the complement of a in $\mathcal{C}$. Thus

$$(\alpha) \; and \; (\beta) \rightarrow ab,$$
$$(\alpha) \; or \; (\beta) \rightarrow (a + b) + ab,$$
$$not \; (\alpha) \rightarrow a + e.$$

Hence the compound statements mentioned above can be expressed in terms of *product* and *sum*. Other operations may be, and frequently are, taken as fundamental but, from our point of view, the advantage of the present choice is that the set of all subclasses of the class $\mathcal{C}$ (or of any other class) forms a *ring B* with the above definitions of product and sum. This was shown in §2 and, furthermore, it is clear that in order to get a ring it is not

necessary to have *all* subclasses of a given class but merely
a system of subclasses which contains the sum and product
of any two of its members.

The zero of the ring B is the void class d of $\mathcal{C}$, which we
may conveniently denote by 0, as usual. It is clear that

$$\text{(i)} \quad x^2 = x,$$
$$\text{(ii)} \quad x + x = 0,$$
$$\text{(iii)} \quad xy = yx,$$

for arbitrary x, y in B. Furthermore, these are true for the
elements of a ring of subclasses of any class. Thus we are
led naturally to a study of rings with these properties. It
will appear presently that property (i) implies the other
two, and we shall show eventually (Theorem 42) that *any*
ring with property (i) is isomorphic to a ring of subclasses
of some class.

32. Boolean rings. We now give the following general
definition. A *Boolean ring* is a ring of more than one
element with the property that

$$(35) \qquad\qquad x^2 = x$$

for every element x. It is at once evident that a ring of
subclasses of a given class is an example of a Boolean ring.
Also the ring I_2 of integers modulo 2 is a Boolean ring of
two elements which is, in fact, isomorphic to the ring of all
subclasses of a class of one element. Another example of a
Boolean ring is the set of four elements 0, 1, a, b, where 0
is the zero and 1 the unit element, sums and products being
otherwise defined by:

$$a + b = b + a = 1, a + 1 = 1 + a = b, b + 1 =$$
$$1 + b = a,$$
$$1 + 1 = 0, a + a = 0, b + b = 0, ab = ba = 0,$$
$$a^2 = a, b^2 = b.$$

The reader may be interested in verifying that this ring is isomorphic to the ring of all subclasses of a two-element class.

We proceed to prove some properties of an arbitrary Boolean ring. Let a be any element of the Boolean ring B. By applying (35) to the element $2a$, we see that $4a^2 = 2a$. But $a^2 = a$; hence $4a = 2a$, or $2a = 0$. Thus *a Boolean ring has characteristic* 2. Hence, in particular, $x = -x$ for every x in B.

It is now easy to show that *a Boolean ring is necessarily commutative*. Let a and b be any elements of B, and apply (35) to $a + b$; thus

$$(a + b)^2 = a^2 + ab + ba + b^2 = a + b.$$

Since $a^2 = a$, $b^2 = b$, it follows that $ab + ba = 0$. That is, $ab = -ba = ba$, and B is commutative.

In view of (35), it is clear that a Boolean ring can not have nonzero nilpotent elements; hence, by Theorem 32, a Boolean ring with a finite number of elements must be isomorphic to a complete direct sum of a finite number of fields. Now a homomorphic image of a Boolean ring is either a one-element ring or a Boolean ring, and thus each of these fields is of characteristic 2 and has the property that $x^2 = x$ for every element x. By Theorem 16, any such field is isomorphic to the two-element field I_2 of integers modulo 2. Clearly a complete direct sum of k fields I_2 has exactly 2^k elements, and also has a unit element. We have therefore established the following result:

THEOREM 39. *A finite Boolean ring has* 2^k *elements for some positive integer* k. *It has a unit element and is isomorphic to the complete direct sum of* k *fields* I_2 .

As an illustration of this theorem, it may be observed that the four-element Boolean ring exhibited above is isomorphic to the direct sum of two rings I_2 by the correspondence:

$$0 \leftrightarrow (0', 0'), \qquad a \leftrightarrow (1', 0'),$$
$$1 \leftrightarrow (1', 1'), \qquad b \leftrightarrow (0', 1').$$

From Theorem 39 we can prove

THEOREM 40. *A finite Boolean ring is isomorphic to the ring of all subclasses of some finite class.*

To prove this, let B be a finite Boolean ring which is isomorphic to the complete direct sum of k fields I_2 by a correspondence

$$(36) \qquad x \leftrightarrow (x_1, x_2, \cdots, x_k),$$

each x_i naturally being either $0'$ or $1'$. Let us denote the homomorphism $x \to x_i$ of B onto I_2 by h_i, and let H be the class of all h_i $(i = 1, 2, \cdots, k)$. Now if a is any element of B let a^* be the class of all h_i such that $h_i(a) = 1'$. By the correspondence

$$(37) \qquad a \to a^*,$$

each element of B therefore corresponds to a subclass of H. Since (36) is an isomorphism of B with the complete direct sum of k fields I_2, it follows that (37) is a one-to-one correspondence of elements of B with *all* subclasses of H for, by (36), an element of B is completely determined by the distribution of the elements $1'$ in the corresponding element of the direct sum.

Now $h_i(ab) = h_i(a)h_i(b)$; hence $h_i(ab) = 1'$ if and only if $h_i(a) = 1'$ and $h_i(b) = 1'$. Thus, by the correspondence (37), $ab \to a^*b^*$, where as usual a^*b^* denotes the class of elements in both a^* and b^*. Furthermore, since $h_i(a + b) = h_i(a) + h_i(b)$, we have $h_i(a + b) = 1'$ if and only if one of $h_i(a), h_i(b)$ is $0'$ and the other is $1'$. Thus $a + b \to a^* + b^*$, where $a^* + b^*$ is the subclass of H consisting of those elements in a^* or in b^* but not in both. It follows that (37) is the desired isomorphism of B with the ring of all subclasses of the class H, and the theorem is established.

In the two preceding theorems, the finiteness of B has played an important part, and there are only partial analogues of these theorems for unrestricted Boolean rings. For example, the ring of all finite subclasses of an infinite class is a Boolean ring without a unit element, which clearly can not be isomorphic to a complete direct sum of fields since such a direct sum does have a unit element. However, we shall now prove

THEOREM 41. *A necessary and sufficient condition that a ring be isomorphic to a subdirect sum of fields I_2 is that it be a Boolean ring.*

It is obvious that a subdirect sum of fields I_2 is a Boolean ring. Conversely, since a homomorphic image of a Boolean ring is a one-element ring or a Boolean ring, Theorem 34 shows that a Boolean ring is isomorphic to a subdirect sum of subdirectly irreducible Boolean rings. However, by Theorem 35, a subdirectly irreducible Boolean ring is a field, which must be isomorphic to I_2 as shown in the proof of Theorem 39.

In extending Theorem 40 to arbitrary Boolean rings, one may proceed as in the proof of that theorem except that H may now be an infinite set and the correspondence (37) is not necessarily an isomorphism of B with the ring of *all* subclasses of H but with a subring of this ring. We thus have

THEOREM 42. *Any Boolean ring is isomorphic to a ring of subclasses of some class.*

Since, conversely, a ring of subclasses of any class is a Boolean ring, this fundamental result shows that the study of Boolean rings is coextensive with the study of rings of classes. As a matter of fact, *all* the formal properties of classes relative to union and intersection are logical consequences of the defining properties of a Boolean ring.

We next turn to some generalizations which are of algebraic interest but which are no longer associated with the algebra of classes.

33. The p-rings. Perhaps the most obvious generalization of a Boolean ring is that obtained by replacing (35) by $x^n = x$ for some fixed positive integer n. It turns out that the case in which n is a prime is of central interest in that the analogy with Boolean rings is more perfect than for composite n.

We let p be a fixed prime, and make the following definition. A ring R of more than one element is a *p-ring* if for every element x of R,

$$(38) \qquad x^p = x, \qquad px = 0.$$

It is clear that a Boolean ring is a 2-ring, and in this special case the second of conditions (38) is a consequence of the first. However, this is not true in general as is shown by the example of a Boolean ring, whose elements satisfy the equation $x^2 = x$ and therefore also satisfy the equation $x^3 = x$. The characteristic is 2 instead of 3, and therefore $x^3 = x$ for all elements of a ring does not imply that the characteristic is 3. Accordingly, we include both conditions (38) in the definition of a p-ring.

For each p, we already know one p-ring, namely, the field I_p as shown in §5. It will presently appear that I_p plays essentially the same role in the study of p-rings that I_2 does in the case of Boolean rings.

THEOREM 43. *A p-ring R is necessarily commutative.*

The proof is somewhat more difficult than the corresponding result for Boolean rings. We shall give the proof for the case in which $p = 5$ as this will sufficiently illustrate the general method. We accordingly assume that R is a 5-ring, and let a and b be any two elements of R. It is not difficult to verify that

$$(39) \quad (a + b)^5 = a^5 + A_1 + A_2 + A_3 + A_4 + b^5,$$

where

$$(40) \quad A_1 = a^4b + a^3ba + a^2ba^2 + aba^3 + ba^4,$$

and A_i ($i = 2, 3, 4$) is a sum of products of a and b, in each term of which b appears i times and a appears $5 - i$ times. Since $(a + b)^5 = a + b$, it follows from (39) that

$$(41) \quad A_1 + A_2 + A_3 + A_4 = 0.$$

Furthermore, this equation has been obtained by starting with arbitrary a and b; it must therefore remain true if we replace b in turn by $2b, 3b, 4b$. However, if in A_i we replace b by jb the result is just $j^i A_i$, so we get the following system of equations:

$$(42) \quad \begin{aligned} A_1 + A_2 + A_3 + A_4 &= 0, \\ 2A_1 + 2^2A_2 + 2^3A_3 + 2^4A_4 &= 0, \\ 3A_1 + 3^2A_2 + 3^3A_3 + 3^4A_4 &= 0, \\ 4A_1 + 4^2A_2 + 4^3A_3 + 4^4A_4 &= 0. \end{aligned}$$

Now let us set

$$m = \begin{vmatrix} 1 & 1 & 1 & 1 \\ 2 & 2^2 & 2^3 & 2^4 \\ 3 & 3^2 & 3^3 & 3^4 \\ 4 & 4^2 & 4^3 & 4^4 \end{vmatrix},$$

and denote the co-factors of the elements in the first column by m_1, m_2, m_3, m_4, respectively. If we multiply the equations (42) by these respective co-factors and add, an elementary property of determinants shows that $mA_1 = 0$. Now the determinant m is a Vandermonde determinant, and it is known that m is equal to a product of positive integers, each of which is less than 5. Hence $(5, m) = (1)$, and there therefore exist integers r, s such that $5r + ms = 1$. Since R has characteristic 5, and $mA_1 = 0$, it follows that

$$A_1 = (5r + ms)A_1 = 0.$$

An easy calculation, making use of the expression (40) for A_1, will show that

$$aA_1 - A_1a = ab - ba.$$

Since $A_1 = 0$, this implies that $ab = ba$, and therefore R is commutative.

The other theorems about p-rings which we shall mention are completely analogous in statement and proof to the corresponding theorems for Boolean rings.

First, we observe that a p-ring can not have any nonzero nilpotent elements and also that a homomorphic image of a p-ring is a p-ring or a one-element ring. Hence the proofs of Theorems 39 and 41 may be easily modified so as to establish the following more general results:

THEOREM 44. *A finite p-ring has p^k elements for some positive integer k. It has a unit element and is isomorphic to the complete direct sum of k fields I_p.*

THEOREM 45. *A necessary and sufficient condition that a ring be isomorphic to a subdirect sum of fields I_p is that it be a p-ring.*

This concludes our brief remarks about p-rings. As a

matter of fact, it can be shown that if for each element x of a ring R there exists an integer $n > 1$, depending on x, such that $x^n = x$, then R is commutative. However, we do not give a proof as no strictly elementary proof is known. Theorem 46, of the following section, will show that such a ring is isomorphic to a subdirect sum of fields. In this case, however, the fields need not all be identical.

34. **Regular rings.** Some of the results we have obtained for p-rings can be suitably modified so as to apply to an even more general class of rings. A ring R is called a *regular ring** if for each element a of R there exists an element x of R such that

$$(43) \qquad axa = a.$$

If a happens to have an inverse, this equation is clearly satisfied by $x = a^{-1}$; while if $a = 0$, x may be any element of R. Since in a division ring every nonzero element has an inverse, it follows that every division ring is regular. In particular, then, every field is a commutative regular ring. Furthermore, a p-ring is regular since equation (43) is satisfied by $x = a^{p-2}$ if $p > 2$, and by $x = a$ if $p = 2$.

We now show that a regular ring has zero Jacobson radical. Let a be any element of the Jacobson radical of a regular ring, and assume that x is an element satisfying equation (43). Then $a(-x)$ must be quasi-regular, and hence there exists an element b such that

$$-ax + b - axb = 0.$$

If we multiply this on the left by ax and substitute from (43), we see that $-ax = 0$. Since $axa = a$, it follows that $a = 0$.

In view of this result, Theorem 38 establishes

* Not to be confused with the notion of quasi-regularity.

THEOREM 46. *Every commutative regular ring of more than one element is isomorphic to a subdirect sum of fields.*

From this theorem it is clear that a *commutative* regular ring can have no nonzero nilpotent element. This can also be seen directly since repeated multiplication of (43) by ax shows that $a^{n+1}x^n = a$ for every positive integer n.

An alternate proof of Theorem 46 can be based on Theorems 34 and 35, as was done in the proof of Theorem 41.

It is easy to verify that a complete direct sum of regular rings is a regular ring and therefore, in particular, a complete direct sum of fields is regular. Theorem 31 then leads to the following interesting result:

THEOREM 47. *A commutative ring R is a subring of some commutative regular ring if and only if R has zero radical.*

In view of Theorem 32, we also have

THEOREM 48. *A commutative ring with only a finite number of ideals is a regular ring if and only if it has zero radical.*

Finally, we shall establish the following characterization of the commutative regular rings:

THEOREM 49. *A commutative ring R is a regular ring if and only if every ideal in R coincides with its radical.*

First, let R be regular, $\mathfrak{a}$ any ideal in R and $\mathfrak{r}$ the radical of $\mathfrak{a}$. Since always $\mathfrak{a} \subseteq \mathfrak{r}$, we only need to prove that $\mathfrak{r} \subseteq \mathfrak{a}$. Let $a = a^2x$ be any element of $\mathfrak{r}$, so that $a^i \varepsilon \mathfrak{a}$ for some positive integer i. If $i > 1$, then $a = a^i x^{i-1}$, so $a \varepsilon \mathfrak{a}$ and thus $\mathfrak{r} \subseteq \mathfrak{a}$.

Conversely, suppose that R is a commutative ring in which every ideal coincides with its radical. Let a be any element of R and consider the ideal $\mathfrak{a}$ consisting of the elements a^2y, $y \varepsilon R$. Clearly $a^3 \equiv 0(\mathfrak{a})$, so that a is in the radical of $\mathfrak{a}$ and hence, by hypothesis, $a \equiv 0(\mathfrak{a})$. That is, there is an element y_1 of R such that $a^2y_1 = a$. This shows that R is a regular ring and completes the proof of the theorem.

REFERENCES

A good introduction to the algebra of logic will be found in Birkhoff and MacLane [1], Chapter XI.

Boolean rings were first considered by Stone. See Stone [1] for a detailed account of the properties of these rings.

The p-rings are briefly discussed in McCoy and Montgomery [1].

For a proof that a ring is commutative if all its elements satisfy an equation $x^n = x$, see Jacobson [3]; Forsythe and McCoy [1].

Regular rings were introduced by von Neumann and discussed in von Neumann [1], [2]. See also Forsythe and McCoy [1]; McCoy [1].

CHAPTER VIII

RINGS OF MATRICES

35. **Introduction.** In §2 of Chapter I, we introduced, as an illustration of the concept of ring, the ring of all real matrices of order 2, and suggested that this example could be generalized in at least two different ways. In the present chapter we shall make these generalizations and study matrices in some detail. The necessary definitions will be given presently, but first we make a few remarks which will help to put the rest of the chapter in proper perspective.

The importance of the theory of matrices stems from at least two facts. In the first place, the theory furnishes a convenient approach to the study of *linear transformations*, which are fundamental in many branches of mathematics. In the second place, it turns out that a great many rings are isomorphic to suitably chosen rings of matrices with, say, real or complex elements, and therefore a study of such rings is of quite general interest. Most of the extensive theory of matrices deals with matrices whose elements are from a given *field* or *integral domain*. These important cases are well covered by the readily available texts listed at the end of this chapter, in which the reader will also find adequate treatment of the important aspects of the theory just mentioned. Accordingly, we confine our remarks to a more general situation, and in the following section shall introduce matrices with elements in an arbitrary ring and mention a few fundamental properties. Beginning with §37, the matrices considered will have elements in an arbitrary *commutative* ring with unit element.

The reader who is familiar with the theory of matrices

with elements in a field will recognize all our results as generalizations of well-known theorems. However, it is hoped that the generality of the approach will furnish an additional insight into the theory.

It will be necessary to assume that the reader is familiar with those elementary properties of determinants which are to be found in most texts on the theory of equations.

36. **Definitions and fundamental properties.** Let R denote an arbitrary ring, n a fixed positive integer, and consider square arrays of the form

$$(44) \qquad \begin{bmatrix} a_{11} & a_{12} & \cdots & a_{1n} \\ a_{21} & a_{22} & \cdots & a_{2n} \\ \cdots\cdots\cdots\cdots\cdots\cdots \\ a_{n1} & a_{n2} & \cdots & a_{nn} \end{bmatrix},$$

where $a_{ij} \; \varepsilon \; R \; (i, j = 1, 2, \cdots, n)$. An array (44) will be called a *matrix* or, more precisely, a *matrix of order n*, since it has n rows and columns. It is frequently convenient to write, in place of (44), the abbreviated symbol $\| a_{ij} \|$. Two matrices $\| a_{ij} \|$ and $\| b_{ij} \|$, of the same order n, are to be considered as *equal* if and only if they are identical, that is if and only if $a_{ij} = b_{ij}$, $(i, j = 1, 2, \cdots, n)$.

We now define addition and multiplication of matrices of order n. First, we define

$$(45) \qquad \| a_{ij} \| + \| b_{ij} \| = \| a_{ij} + b_{ij} \|.$$

It is evident that this merely states that for i and j having any fixed values from the set $\{1, 2, \cdots, n\}$, the element in the ith row and jth column of the sum is equal to the sum of the elements in the ith row and jth column of the respective summands.

Multiplication of two matrices is defined by the formula

$$(46) \qquad \| a_{ij} \| \cdot \| b_{ij} \| = \left\| \sum_{k=1}^{n} a_{ik} b_{kj} \right\|.$$

Thus, the element in the ith row and jth column of $\| a_{ij} \| \cdot \| b_{ij} \|$ is the sum of the products of the elements of the ith row of $\| a_{ij} \|$ by the corresponding elements of the jth column of $\| b_{ij} \|$. For example, if $n = 2$, we have the explicit formula

$$\begin{bmatrix} a_{11} & a_{12} \\ a_{21} & a_{22} \end{bmatrix} \cdot \begin{bmatrix} b_{11} & b_{12} \\ b_{21} & b_{22} \end{bmatrix} = \begin{bmatrix} a_{11}b_{11} + a_{12}b_{21} & a_{11}b_{12} + a_{12}b_{22} \\ a_{21}b_{11} + a_{22}b_{21} & a_{21}b_{12} + a_{22}b_{22} \end{bmatrix}.$$

It is not difficult to show that, with the above definitions of addition and multiplication, the set of all matrices of the form (44) is a ring. It is almost obvious that addition has the required properties. To prove the associative law of multiplication, we make use of (46) and the fact that multiplication is associative in R. Thus,

$$\| a_{ij} \| (\| b_{ij} \| \cdot \| c_{ij} \|) = \| a_{ij} \| \cdot \left\| \sum_{k=1}^{n} b_{ik} c_{kj} \right\|$$

$$= \left\| \sum_{l=1}^{n} a_{il} \left(\sum_{k=1}^{n} b_{lk} c_{kj} \right) \right\| = \left\| \sum_{k,l=1}^{n} a_{il} b_{lk} c_{kj} \right\|.$$

A similar calculation will show that $(\| a_{ij} \| \cdot \| b_{ij} \|) \| c_{ij} \|$ yields the same result, and thus multiplication of matrices, as defined by (46), is associative.

The first of the distributive laws is established by the following calculation:

$$\| a_{ij} \| (\| b_{ij} \| + \| c_{ij} \|) = \| a_{ij} \| \cdot \| b_{ij} + c_{ij} \|$$

$$= \left\| \sum_{k=1}^{n} a_{ik}(b_{kj} + c_{kj}) \right\| = \left\| \sum_{k=1}^{n} (a_{ik} b_{kj} + a_{ik} c_{kj}) \right\|$$

$$= \left\| \sum_{k=1}^{n} a_{ik} b_{kj} + \sum_{k=1}^{n} a_{ik} c_{kj} \right\| = \left\| \sum_{k=1}^{n} a_{ik} b_{kj} \right\|$$

$$+ \left\| \sum_{k=1}^{n} a_{ik} c_{kj} \right\| = \| a_{ij} \| \cdot \| b_{ij} \| + \| a_{ij} \| \cdot \| c_{ij} \|.$$

The other distributive law follows in like manner.

We have thus shown that, with the definitions (45) and (46) of addition and multiplication, the set of all matrices (44) is a ring, which we shall henceforth denote by R_n. An element A of the ring R_n is thus a matrix of order n. If A is the matrix (44), each a_{ij} may be called an *element* of the matrix A and thus, more precisely, the ring R_n is the *ring of all matrices of order n with elements in the ring R.*

From (45), it is easy to verify that if 0 is the zero element of R, then

$$\begin{bmatrix} 0 & 0 & \cdots & 0 \\ 0 & 0 & \cdots & 0 \\ \cdots\cdots\cdots\cdots\cdots \\ 0 & 0 & \cdots & 0 \end{bmatrix}$$

is the zero of R_n. Similarly, if R has the unit element 1, R_n has the unit element

$$(47) \qquad \begin{bmatrix} 1 & 0 & \cdots & 0 \\ 0 & 1 & \cdots & 0 \\ \cdots\cdots\cdots\cdots\cdots \\ 0 & 0 & \cdots & 1 \end{bmatrix},$$

it being understood that this matrix has the element 1 along the main diagonal and zeros elsewhere.

A matrix of the special form

$$(48) \qquad \begin{bmatrix} a & 0 & \cdots & 0 \\ 0 & a & \cdots & 0 \\ \cdots\cdots\cdots\cdots\cdots \\ 0 & 0 & \cdots & a \end{bmatrix}$$

is sometimes called a *scalar* matrix. It is readily verified that the set of all scalar matrices in R_n is a subring of R_n

which is isomorphic to R and, in accordance with the principle explained in §17, we shall find it convenient to identify the matrix (48) with the element a of R. Thus, in particular, 0 will indicate the zero of R_n as well as that of R; and if R has a unit element 1, the unit element of R_n will be denoted by the same symbol 1. It may be emphasized that the equation $A = 0$ means that the matrix A is the zero matrix, that is, that *all* elements a_{ij} of A are zero.

Multiplication by a scalar matrix is particularly simple. Thus, if $A = \| a_{ij} \|$,

$$
aA = \begin{bmatrix} a & 0 & \cdots & 0 \\ 0 & a & \cdots & 0 \\ \cdots\cdots\cdots\cdots \\ 0 & 0 & \cdots & a \end{bmatrix} \begin{bmatrix} a_{11} & a_{12} & \cdots & a_{1n} \\ a_{21} & a_{22} & \cdots & a_{2n} \\ \cdots\cdots\cdots\cdots\cdots \\ a_{n1} & a_{n2} & \cdots & a_{nn} \end{bmatrix}
$$

$$
= \begin{bmatrix} aa_{11} & aa_{12} & \cdots & aa_{1n} \\ aa_{21} & aa_{22} & \cdots & aa_{2n} \\ \cdots\cdots\cdots\cdots\cdots \\ aa_{n1} & aa_{n2} & \cdots & aa_{nn} \end{bmatrix}.
$$

It has already been pointed out in Chapter I that even if R is a field, R_2 is not commutative and also has proper divisors of zero. Thus, if $n > 1$, R_n is not commutative even if R is, and has proper divisors of zero even though R has none. However, as pointed out above, the existence of a unit element in R implies the existence of a unit element in R_n.

There is one further instance in which a property of R is carried over to R_n, and we shall mention it without proof. It will be recalled from §34 that a *regular ring* R is a ring such that $axa = a$ has a solution x for every element a of R. It has been proved by von Neumann that if R is a regular ring with unit element then, for each positive integer n, R_n is a regular ring with unit element.

For some purposes, matrices with elements in a polynomial ring are of special interest. Let $R[\lambda]$ be the ring of polynomials in the indeterminate λ, with coefficients in the arbitrary ring R. Then $R[\lambda]_n$ is the ring of all matrices of order n with elements in $R[\lambda]$. For example, if $a, b, \cdots , h$ are elements of R, the matrix

$$(49) \qquad \begin{bmatrix} a\lambda^2 + b\lambda + c & d\lambda + e \\ f\lambda^2 + g\lambda & h\lambda \end{bmatrix}$$

is an element of $R[\lambda]_2$. To this element of $R[\lambda]_2$, we now make correspond the unique polynomial in λ with coefficients from R_2,

$$(50) \qquad \begin{bmatrix} a & 0 \\ f & 0 \end{bmatrix} \lambda^2 + \begin{bmatrix} b & d \\ g & h \end{bmatrix} \lambda + \begin{bmatrix} c & e \\ 0 & 0 \end{bmatrix}.$$

This is an element of $R_2[\lambda]$, and the general correspondence of elements of $R[\lambda]_2$ with those of $R_2[\lambda]$, illustrated by the correspondence of (49) and (50), is seen to be an isomorphism of these two rings. More generally, we see that $R[\lambda]_n$ and $R_n[\lambda]$ are isomorphic, and thus we have an alternative way of looking at a matrix of order n with elements in $R[\lambda]$, namely, as a polynomial in λ with coefficients in R_n.

37. Determinants and systems of linear homogeneous equations. In this section, and henceforth in this chapter, R shall be a *commutative ring of more than one element and with unit element* 1. Hence always $aA = Aa$, that is, scalar matrices are commutative with all matrices of R_n.

The theory of determinants is usually developed for the case in which the elements are real or complex numbers but it is easy to show that most of the theory is applicable to determinants with elements in the commutative ring R with unit element. It is obvious that the familiar definition of a determinant may be used, and we shall now illustrate in some detail how the known theorems may be carried over to this more general case.

Consider, for example, the familiar expansion of a determinant in terms of a given row or column and, for concreteness, let the determinant be of order three. We introduce indeterminates x_{ij} $(i, j = 1, 2, 3)$, and consider the polynomial ring $I[x_{11}, \cdots, x_{33}]$, where I is the ring of integers. Thus the determinant

$$\begin{vmatrix} x_{11} & x_{12} & x_{13} \\ x_{21} & x_{22} & x_{23} \\ x_{31} & x_{32} & x_{33} \end{vmatrix}$$

is an element of $I[x_{11}, \cdots, x_{33}]$ which we may denote by $h(x_{11}, \cdots, x_{33})$. Let X_{1j} be the co-factor of x_{1j} in this determinant for $j = 1, 2, 3$; and set

$$k(x_{11}, \cdots, x_{33}) = x_{11}X_{11} + x_{12}X_{12} + x_{13}X_{13}.$$

By a familiar theorem on determinants, if c_{ij} $(i, j = 1, 2, 3)$ are any real or complex numbers—in particular, any positive integers—then

$$h(c_{11}, \cdots, c_{33}) = k(c_{11}, \cdots, c_{33}).$$

Theorem 11 then shows that

$$h(a_{11}, \cdots, a_{33}) = k(a_{11}, \cdots, a_{33}),$$

where the a_{ij} are arbitrary elements of R. This merely means, however, that a determinant with elements in R can be expanded in terms of the first row by the usual formula. In like manner, one can establish all the usual expansion theorems for determinants and, for the most part, we shall assume these without further comment. In particular, we shall several times have occasion to use the fact that the sum of the products of the elements of the kth row (column) of a determinant by the co-factors of the corresponding elements of the lth row (column) is zero if $k \neq l$, and is equal to the determinant itself if $k = l$.

Now let $A = \| a_{ij} \|$, $B = \| b_{ij} \|$ be given elements of R_n, that is, matrices with elements in R. Corresponding to the matrix A we may form its determinant and denote it by $| A |$ or by $| a_{ij} |$. Since the rule given above for multiplying matrices is just the familiar row by column rule for multiplying determinants, we have the important result that

$$(51) \qquad | AB | = | A | \cdot | B |.$$

From the matrix A we may construct the so-called *adjoint* matrix

$$\text{adj } A = \begin{bmatrix} A_{11} & A_{21} & \cdots & A_{n1} \\ A_{12} & A_{22} & \cdots & A_{n2} \\ \cdots\cdots\cdots\cdots\cdots\cdots \\ A_{1n} & A_{2n} & \cdots & A_{nn} \end{bmatrix},$$

where A_{ij} is the co-factor of a_{ij} in $| A |$. An easy calculation, making use of a remark above, shows that

$$A(\text{adj } A) = (\text{adj } A)A = \begin{bmatrix} | A | & 0 & \cdots & 0 \\ 0 & | A | & \cdots & 0 \\ \cdots\cdots\cdots\cdots\cdots\cdots \\ 0 & 0 & \cdots & | A | \end{bmatrix},$$

which we shall write in the more convenient form

(52) $A(\operatorname{adj} A) = (\operatorname{adj} A)A = |A|.$

We may now easily prove

THEOREM 50. *The element A of R_n has an inverse in R_n if and only if $|A|$ has an inverse in R.*

First, if $AB = BA = 1$, it follows from (51) that $|B|$ is the inverse of $|A|$. Conversely, if $|A|$ has an inverse d in R, it is clear from (52) that $d(\operatorname{adj} A)$ is the inverse of A.

So far we have been able to carry over a number of familiar theorems on determinants because these results take the form of identities in the elements considered as arbitrary variables. However, certain difficulties arise in many applications of the theory. For example, in the usual study of systems of linear equations by means of determinants, use is frequently made of the process of division by a nonzero determinant. In case the elements are from an arbitrary commutative ring, there may well be proper divisors of zero and this process is then impossible. Accordingly, the subject must be approached with considerable care.

We now pass to a consideration of the following system of linear homogeneous equations,

(53) $$\sum_{j=1}^{n} c_{ij} x_j = 0 \qquad (i = 1, 2, \cdots, m),$$

where the coefficients c_{ij} are elements of R and a solution $(x_1, x_2, \cdots, x_n)$ is sought in R. In accordance with the usual procedure, let us consider the array or matrix* M of the coefficients of the unknowns in the system (53).

---

* This is the only place where we shall use the term *matrix* for an array which may not be square. However, it is the usual terminology of the theory of equations, and our purpose is to find a result analogous to the well-known one of that theory.

In particular, we shall be concerned with the *rank* of M which we proceed to define.

If Q is a set of elements of R and a is an element of R such that the product of a by every element of Q is zero, we may say that a is an *annihilator* of the set Q. Thus, if Q consist of the zero alone, any element of R is an annihilator of Q. If R has no proper divisors of zero, a set Q of elements of R has a nonzero annihilator if and only if Q contains only the zero element.

If the set of all elements c_{ij} of M has a nonzero annihilator, M is said to have *rank* zero. If M does not have rank zero, its *rank* is the greatest positive integer r such that the set of all determinants of square minors of M of order r does not have a nonzero annihilator. It follows easily that if M has square minors of order $s > r$, the set of all determinants of square minors of order s has a nonzero annihilator.

It is obvious that the equations (53) always have the trivial solution $(0, 0, \cdots, 0)$. We now prove

THEOREM 51. *The system* (53) *has a nontrivial solution if and only if the rank of the matrix of the coefficients is less than the number of unknowns.*

First, let us assume that there exists a solution $(a_1, a_2, \cdots, a_n)$ with $a_k \neq 0$, and prove that the rank of M is less than n. This is obviously true if $m < n$, so we may assume that $m \geq n$. Consider any determinant D of order n which can be formed from M and, for convenience of notation, suppose that its elements come from the first n rows of M. Now, by hypothesis, we have

$$\sum_{j=1}^{n} c_{ij} a_j = 0 \quad (i = 1, 2 \cdots, m).$$

If we multiply the first of these equations by the co-factor of c_{1k} in D and, in general, the i-th equation by the co-factor of c_{ik} in D, and add for $i = 1, 2, \cdots, n$, we get $a_k D = 0$. A similar calculation will show that the product of a_k by *every* determinant of order n which can be formed from M is zero. Since $a_k \neq 0$, this means that the rank of M is less than n.

Now let us assume that the rank of M is $r < n$. If it happens that $r = m$, we may replace the system (53) by an equivalent system consisting of the equations (53) together with another equation in which all the coefficients are zero. Thus there is no loss of generality in assuming, as we now do, that $r < m$. Let a be a nonzero element of R, whose existence is asserted by the definition of rank, which annihilates the set of all determinants of square minors of M of order $r + 1$. If $r = 0$, then clearly $x_j = a$, $(j = 1, 2, \cdots, n)$, is a nontrivial solution of the system (53). Hence suppose that $r > 0$. It follows that the product of a by the determinant of some minor of M of order r is different from zero and let us suppose, for convenience of notation, that this minor is in the upper left-hand corner of M. Let $d_1, d_2, \cdots, d_{r+1}$ be the respective co-factors of the elements in the last row of the determinant of order $r + 1$ formed from the elements of M in the upper left-hand corner. We shall show that

$$x_j = a d_j \quad (j = 1, 2, \cdots, r + 1),$$
$$x_j = 0 \quad (j = r + 2, \cdots, n),$$

is a solution of the equations (53), and it is certainly nontrivial since, by our agreement, $x_{r+1} = a d_{r+1} \neq 0$. If these values of the unknowns are substituted in equations (53), the first r equations are satisfied since the sum of the products of the elements of any row of a determinant by the co-factors of the corresponding elements of a different row is always zero. When these values are substituted in the left-hand side of any one of the remaining equations, we get the product of a by the determinant of a square minor of M of order $r + 1$, which is zero by our choice of a. The theorem is therefore established.

Before turning to other matters, we prove the following

COROLLARY. *An element $A = \| a_{ij} \|$ of R_n is a divisor of zero in R_n if and only if $| A |$ is a divisor of zero in R.*

Now A is a divisor of zero in R_n if and only if there exists a nonzero element $X = \| x_{ij} \|$ of R_n such that $AX = 0$, or a nonzero element $Y = \| y_{ij} \|$ of R_n such that $YA = 0$. Suppose that $AX = 0$ with $x_{kl} \neq 0$. Then, by the definition of multiplication in R_n we must have, from a consideration of the elements of the lth column of the product AX,

$$\sum_{j=1}^{n} a_{ij} x_{jl} = 0 \qquad (i = 1, 2, \cdots, n).$$

It follows from the preceding theorem that the rank of the matrix A is less than n, that is, that $| A |$ is a divisor of zero in R.

On the other hand, if $YA = 0$ with $y_{kl} \neq 0$, the elements of the kth row of the product give

$$\sum_{j=1}^{n} a_{ji} y_{kj} = 0 \qquad (i = 1, 2, \cdots, n).$$

The matrix of this system is that obtained from A by interchange of rows and columns, so its determinant is still $| A |$, which must be a divisor of zero by the same argument. Hence if A is a divisor of zero in R_n it follows that $| A |$ is a divisor of zero in R.

The converse is almost obvious. For if $| A |$ is a divisor of zero there exist, by Theorem 51, elements z_j of R, not all zero, such that

$$\sum_{j=1}^{n} a_{ij} z_j = 0 \qquad (i = 1, 2, \cdots, n).$$

Hence $AZ = 0$, where Z is the nonzero matrix with $z_1, z_2, \cdots, z_n$ as elements of the first column and all other elements zero. Thus A is a divisor of zero in R_n.

In §40, we shall consider some further questions about divisors of zero in rings of matrices.

38. Characteristic ideal and null ideal of a matrix. Let $A = \| a_{ij} \|$ be a given matrix of R_n, and λ an indeterminate. With each element

$$g(\lambda) = g_0 \lambda^k + g_1 \lambda^{k-1} + \cdots + g_k$$

of the polynomial ring $R[\lambda]$, we may associate the matrix

$$g(A) = g_0 A^k + g_1 A^{k-1} + \cdots + g_k,$$

it being understood that the g_i are now to be interpreted as scalar matrices. Since scalar matrices are commutative with all matrices, it follows readily that the correspondence

$$g(\lambda) \rightarrow g(A)$$

defines a homomorphism of $R[\lambda]$ into R_n. The kernel of this homomorphism, that is, the ideal of all elements $h(\lambda)$ of $R[\lambda]$ such that $h(A) = 0$, will be called the *null ideal* of A and generally denoted by $\mathfrak{n}$. The ring of the images of elements of $R[\lambda]$ under this homomorphism, in other words, the ring of all polynomials $g(A)$ with coefficients from R, is a commutative subring of R_n which we shall denote by $R[A]$. Since the image of an element of R is the corresponding scalar matrix, it is clear that $R[A]$ contains all scalar matrices. We may also point out that, by the fundamental theorem on homomorphisms,

$$R[A] \cong R[\lambda]/\mathfrak{n},$$

where $\mathfrak{n}$ is the null ideal of A. Later on, we shall determine $\mathfrak{n}$, but first we need some preliminary results.

In the first place, we remark that if R is the field C of complex numbers (or any other field) the null ideal $\mathfrak{n}$ will be a principal ideal. Its generator is usually called the *minimum function* of the matrix A, but we shall not be able to use this concept since, in general, $\mathfrak{n}$ will not be a principal ideal. In the theory of matrices with elements in C, the linear factors of the minimum function are of considerable interest. It will be observed that, in the general case under discussion here, the prime ideals which contain the null ideal play a role similar to that of the linear factors of the minimum function in the classical theory.

We now form the matrix

$$\lambda - A = \begin{bmatrix} \lambda - a_{11} & -a_{12} & \cdots & -a_{1n} \\ -a_{21} & \lambda - a_{22} & \cdots & -a_{2n} \\ \cdots\cdots\cdots\cdots\cdots\cdots\cdots\cdots\cdots \\ -a_{n1} & -a_{n2} & \cdots & \lambda - a_{nn} \end{bmatrix},$$

where λ is an indeterminate, and set

$$(54) \quad f(\lambda) = |\lambda - A| = \lambda^n + a_1\lambda^{n-1} + a_2\lambda^{n-2} + \cdots + a_n.$$

Thus, $f(\lambda)$ is an element of $R[\lambda]$ associated in a definite way with the element A of R_n. The polynomial $f(\lambda)$ is called the *characteristic polynomial* of A, and the principal ideal $(f(\lambda))$ in $R[\lambda]$ is the *characteristic ideal* of A. It is important to note that the constant term a_n of $f(\lambda)$ is just $(-1)^n |A|$.

THEOREM·52. *Any monic polynomial in $R[\lambda]$ of degree n is the characteristic polynomial of some matrix in R_n.*

The case in which $n = 4$ will sufficiently illustrate the general method of proof. If

$$k(\lambda) = \lambda^4 + b_1\lambda^3 + b_2\lambda^2 + b_3\lambda + b_4$$

is an arbitrary monic polynomial of degree 4, we shall show that $k(\lambda)$ is the characteristic polynomial of the matrix

$$B = \begin{bmatrix} 0 & 1 & 0 & 0 \\ 0 & 0 & 1 & 0 \\ 0 & 0 & 0 & 1 \\ -b_4 & -b_3 & -b_2 & -b_1 \end{bmatrix}.$$

In the determinant

$$|\lambda - B| = \begin{vmatrix} \lambda & -1 & 0 & 0 \\ 0 & \lambda & -1 & 0 \\ 0 & 0 & \lambda & -1 \\ b_4 & b_3 & b_2 & \lambda + b_1 \end{vmatrix},$$

multiply the fourth column by λ and add to the third, then multiply the new third column by λ and add to the second, and so on. There results

$$|\lambda - B| = \begin{vmatrix} 0 & -1 & 0 & 0 \\ 0 & 0 & -1 & 0 \\ 0 & 0 & 0 & -1 \\ k(\lambda) & * & * & * \end{vmatrix},$$

where the elements marked $*$ are unspecified since they have no effect on the value of the determinant. Expansion of this determinant in terms of the first column shows that its value is $k(\lambda)$ as required.

As an illustration of the next theorem, let R be the ring $I/(12)$ of integers modulo 12, whose elements we may denote by $0'$ (or 0), $1', \cdots, 11'$; and consider the matrix

$$A^* = \begin{bmatrix} 3' & 6' \\ 0' & 9' \end{bmatrix}.$$

In this case,

$$f(\lambda) = |\lambda - A^*| = \begin{vmatrix} \lambda - 3' & -6' \\ 0' & \lambda - 9' \end{vmatrix} = \lambda^2 + 3',$$

and a simple calculation shows that

$$f(A^*) = \begin{bmatrix} 3' & 6' \\ 0' & 9' \end{bmatrix}^2 + 3' =$$

$$\begin{bmatrix} 9' & 0' \\ 0' & 9' \end{bmatrix} + \begin{bmatrix} 3' & 0' \\ 0' & 3' \end{bmatrix} = \begin{bmatrix} 0' & 0' \\ 0' & 0' \end{bmatrix}.$$

Thus, in our usual notation, $f(A^*) = 0$.

THEOREM 53. *If $f(\lambda)$ is the characteristic polynomial of A, then $f(A) = 0$.*

The proof follows readily from equation (52) as applied to the matrix $\lambda - A$. Thus we have

(55) $(\lambda - A) \operatorname{adj} (\lambda - A) = |\lambda - A| = f(\lambda).$

Now, by definition, $\operatorname{adj}(\lambda - A)$ is seen to be an element of $R[\lambda]_n$ and hence, by the last paragraph of §36, it may be considered as an element of $R_n[\lambda]$. We now apply the Factor Theorem (Theorem 7) in the ring $R_n[\lambda]$, and make use of the fact that $f_R(A) = f_L(A) = f(A)$ since the coefficients of $f(\lambda)$ are scalars and therefore commutative with A. Thus $f(A) = 0$ as required.

In view of the definition of the null ideal $\mathfrak{n}$ of A, it follows from this theorem that $f(\lambda) \varepsilon \mathfrak{n}$. In particular, this implies that $\mathfrak{n} \neq (0)$ since $f(\lambda)$ has the nonzero term λ^n and hence is different from zero.

COROLLARY. *If A has an inverse A^{-1} in R_n, A^{-1} is actually in $R[A]$.*

In view of Theorem 50, if A has an inverse in R_n, $|A|$

has an inverse in R and hence the constant term a_n of the characteristic polynomial $f(\lambda)$ of A, as given in (54), has an inverse in R. Let us set.

$$C = -(A^{n-1} + a_1 A^{n-2} + \cdots + a_{n-1})a_n^{-1}.$$

Using the fact that $f(A) = 0$, it follows by a simple calculation that $AC = CA = 1$, and hence C is the inverse of A.

We are now ready to characterize the null ideal of a matrix. In doing so, we shall again make use of the isomorphism between the rings $R[\lambda]_n$ and $R_n[\lambda]$ described in §36. In particular, the ring $R[\lambda]$ may be regarded as the subring of all scalar matrices of $R[\lambda]_n$ and also as the subring of $R_n[\lambda]$ consisting of polynomials in λ whose coefficients are scalar matrices of R_n. Elements of $R[\lambda]$ are thus commutative with all elements of $R[\lambda]_n$.

THEOREM 54. *If A is an element of R_n with characteristic polynomial $f(\lambda)$ and null ideal $\mathfrak{n}$, then an element $g(\lambda)$ of $R[\lambda]$ is in $\mathfrak{n}$ if and only if there exists an element $K(\lambda)$ of $R[\lambda]_n$ such that*

$$(56) \qquad g(\lambda) \text{ adj } (\lambda - A) = K(\lambda)f(\lambda).$$

First, let us assume that condition (56) is satisfied, and let us multiply by $\lambda - A$ on the right. From (55) it follows that

$$g(\lambda)f(\lambda) = K(\lambda)(\lambda - A)f(\lambda).$$

Now $f(\lambda)$, being a monic polynomial, is not a divisor of zero in $R_n[\lambda]$, and hence we have

$$(57) \qquad g(\lambda) = K(\lambda)(\lambda - A).$$

As in the proof of Theorem 53, the Factor Theorem then shows that $g(A) = 0$, and thus $g(\lambda) \; \varepsilon \; \mathfrak{n}$.

Conversely, suppose that $g(\lambda)$ ε $\mathfrak{n}$, and hence that $g(A) = 0$. It follows from the Factor Theorem that there exists an element $K(\lambda)$ of $R_n[\lambda]$ such that

$$g(\lambda) = K(\lambda)(\lambda - A).$$

From this we see that

$$g(\lambda)\text{adj}(\lambda - A) = K(\lambda)(\lambda - A)\,\text{adj}\,(\lambda - A) = K(\lambda)f(\lambda),$$

and the theorem is established.

Since the elements of adj $(\lambda - A)$ are, except possibly for sign, just the determinants of the $(n - 1)$-rowed minors of $\lambda - A$, condition (56) merely states that the product of $g(\lambda)$ by each of these determinants is divisible by $f(\lambda)$.

Let us again consider the matrix A^* with elements in $I/(12)$ which was used to illustrate Theorem 53. The result just proved states that $g(\lambda)$ is in the null ideal $\mathfrak{n}^*$ of A^* if and only if

$$\begin{aligned}
g(\lambda)(\lambda - 3') &\equiv 0(\lambda^2 + 3'), \\
(58) \qquad g(\lambda)(\lambda - 9') &\equiv 0(\lambda^2 + 3'), \\
g(\lambda)6' &\equiv 0(\lambda^2 + 3').
\end{aligned}$$

We proceed to an actual determination of $\mathfrak{n}^*$. First, we may use the division transformation to express any polynomial $g(\lambda)$ in the form

$$g(\lambda) = q(\lambda)(\lambda^2 + 3') + a\lambda + b,$$

and clearly $g(\lambda) \equiv a\lambda + b\ (\lambda^2 + 3')$. Thus, the congruences (58) show that $g(\lambda)$ ε $\mathfrak{n}^*$ if and only if

$$(a\lambda + b)(\lambda - 3') = a\lambda^2 + (b - 3'a)\lambda - 3'b = a(\lambda^2 + 3'),$$

$$(a\lambda + b)(\lambda - 9') = a\lambda^2 + (b - 9'a)\lambda - 9'b = a(\lambda^2 + 3'),$$

$$(a\lambda + b)6' = 0.$$

From the third of these equations we see that $6'a = 6'b = 0$, so that the only possible values of a and b are 0, $2'$, $4'$, $6'$, $8'$, $10'$. It is easily verified that the only nonzero expressions $a\lambda + b$ which also satisfy the first two of these equations are $2'\lambda + 6'$, $4'\lambda$, $6'\lambda + 6'$, $8'\lambda$, $10'\lambda + 6'$; and that these are respectively equal to $2'\lambda + 6'$, $2'(2'\lambda + 6')$, $3'(2'\lambda + 6')$, $4'(2'\lambda + 6')$, $5'(2'\lambda + 6')$. Thus the only polynomials of degree less than 2 which are in $\mathfrak{n}^*$ are just the integral multiples of the single polynomial $2'\lambda + 6'$. Since the characteristic polynomial $\lambda^2 + 3'$ is in $\mathfrak{n}^*$, it follows that $\mathfrak{n}^* = (\lambda^2 + 3', 2'\lambda + 6')$.

We now return to the general case in which A is an element of R_n. By taking determinants of both sides of equation (57), we obtain the

COROLLARY 1. *If* $g(\lambda)\ \varepsilon\ \mathfrak{n}$, *then* $[g(\lambda)]^n\ \varepsilon\ (f(\lambda))$.

This shows, in particular, that $\mathfrak{n}$ is contained in the radical of the characteristic ideal $(f(\lambda))$. However, since also $(f(\lambda)) \subseteq \mathfrak{n}$, it follows that $\mathfrak{n}$ and $(f(\lambda))$ *have the same radical*. Now a *prime* ideal contains a given ideal if and only if it contains the radical of the ideal, and hence $\mathfrak{n}$ and $(f(\lambda))$ are contained in the same prime ideals.

COROLLARY 2. *The minimal prime ideals belonging to the null ideal of a matrix A are precisely the minimal prime ideals belonging to the characteristic ideal of A.*

39. Resultants. We now digress from the theory of matrices as such to give a generalization of the familiar concept of resultant. Incidentally, this may be of some interest in itself since it will help to clarify the concept of an element being *related to* a given ideal, a notion which was introduced in Chapter V. Near the end of the section, the connection with the material of the present chapter will become apparent.

We consider the ring $R[\lambda]$, where λ is an indeterminate and R an arbitrary commutative ring with unit element. If $\mathfrak{a}$ is an ideal in $R[\lambda]$, we recall that $g(\lambda)$ is *related to* $\mathfrak{a}$ if and only if there exists an element $h(\lambda)$ of $R[\lambda]$, not in $\mathfrak{a}$, such that $g(\lambda)h(\lambda) \equiv 0(\mathfrak{a})$. If R happens to be a field, then $\mathfrak{a}$ is a principal ideal $(f(\lambda))$, and if $f(\lambda)$ has positive degree it follows from Theorem 10 that $g(\lambda)$ is related to $(f(\lambda))$ if and only if $g(\lambda)$ and $f(\lambda)$ have a common factor of positive degree. Furthermore, the value of the resultant of $f(\lambda)$ and $g(\lambda)$ furnishes a convenient test as to whether $g(\lambda)$ is related to $(f(\lambda))$. Our purpose is to generalize these results so that they may apply to an arbitrary commutative ring R with unit element.

Let

$$(59) \qquad f(\lambda) = \lambda^n + a_1\lambda^{n-1} + \cdots + a_n$$

be a monic polynomial of degree $n \geq 1$, and

$$(60) \qquad g(\lambda) = b_0\lambda^m + b_1\lambda^{m-1} + \cdots + b_m \qquad (b_0 \neq 0)$$

an arbitrary element of $R[\lambda]$ of degree $m \geq 0$. We now assume that $g(\lambda)$ is related to $(f(\lambda))$ and hence that there exists an element $h(\lambda)$ of $R[\lambda]$, not in $(f(\lambda))$, such that

$$(61) \qquad g(\lambda)h(\lambda) \equiv 0(f(\lambda)).$$

If we set

$$h(\lambda) = q(\lambda)f(\lambda) + r(\lambda)$$

by use of the division transformation, we see that $r(\lambda) \not\equiv 0(f(\lambda))$ and

$$g(\lambda)r(\lambda) \equiv 0(f(\lambda)).$$

Since the degree of $r(\lambda)$ is less than n, there is therefore no loss of generality in assuming, as we now do, that $h(\lambda)$ itself has degree at most $n - 1$. Accordingly, we may write

$$(62) \qquad h(\lambda) = h_0\lambda^{n-1} + h_1\lambda^{n-2} + \cdots + h_{n-1}$$

where not all coefficients h_i are zero since $h(\lambda) \not\equiv 0(f(\lambda))$. A consideration of the degrees shows that the congruence (61) implies the existence of a polynomial $k(\lambda)$ of degree at most $m - 1$ such that

$$(63) \qquad g(\lambda)h(\lambda) = k(\lambda)f(\lambda).$$

For convenience of notation, let us set

$$(64) \qquad k(\lambda) = -(k_0 \lambda^{m-1} + k_1 \lambda^{m-2} + \cdots + k_{m-1}).$$

If now we substitute from equations (59), (60), (62) and (64) in equation (63), and equate the coefficients of the different powers of λ on the two sides, we get the following system of equations:

$$(65)\qquad
\begin{aligned}
k_0 \quad\quad\quad\ + b_0 h_0 &= 0, \\
a_1 k_0 + k_1 \quad + b_1 h_0 + b_0 h_1 &= 0, \\
a_2 k_0 + a_1 k_1 + k_2 + b_2 h_0 + b_1 h_1 + b_0 h_2 &= 0, \\
\cdots\cdots\cdots\cdots\cdots\cdots\cdots\cdots\cdots \\
a_n k_{m-2} + a_{n-1} k_{m-1} + b_m h_{n-2} + b_{m-1} h_{n-1} &= 0, \\
a_n k_{m-1} + b_m h_{n-1} &= 0.
\end{aligned}$$

We have thus shown that if $g(\lambda)$ is related to $(f(\lambda))$ this system of equations, considered as equations in $h_0, h_1, \cdots, h_{n-1}, k_0, k_1, \cdots, k_{m-1}$ as unknowns, has a nontrivial solution.

Conversely, suppose that the equations (65) have a nontrivial solution, and define $h(\lambda)$ and $k(\lambda)$ by (62) and (64) respectively. Actually, in any nontrivial solution, at least one h_i must be different from zero, for if all $h_i = 0$ it follows from the first equation that $k_0 = 0$. The second equation then shows that $k_1 = 0$, and a continuation of this process shows finally that all $k_i = 0$, and the solution is a trivial one contrary to hypothesis. Since the equation (63) is equivalent to the system (65), it follows that if the equations (65) have a nontrivial solution there exists a nonzero polynomial $h(\lambda)$ of degree at most $n - 1$, and therefore not in $(f(\lambda))$, such that $g(\lambda)h(\lambda) \equiv 0(f(\lambda))$. This means that $g(\lambda)$ is related to $(f(\lambda))$.

These remarks show that $g(\lambda)$ is related to $(f(\lambda))$ if and only if the equations (65) have a nontrivial solution and, by Theorem 51, this is the case if and only if the rank of the matrix of the coefficients is less than $m + n$. However, this is a square matrix of order $m + n$ and hence its rank will be less than $m + n$ if and only if the determinant of the coefficient matrix is a divisor of zero.

In accordance with the usual terminology, we define the *resultant* $\mathcal{R}(f, g)$ of $f(\lambda)$ and $g(\lambda)$ by the determinant

(66) $\mathcal{R}(f, g) =$

$$
\begin{vmatrix}
1 & a_1 & \cdot & \cdot & \cdot & a_n & & & \\
 & 1 & a_1 & \cdot & \cdot & \cdot & a_n & & \\
\cdot & \cdot & \cdot & \cdot & \cdot & \cdot & \cdot & \cdot & \\
 & & & 1 & a_1 & \cdot & \cdot & \cdot & a_n \\
b_0 & b_1 & \cdot & \cdot & \cdot & b_m & & & \\
 & b_0 & b_1 & \cdot & \cdot & \cdot & b_m & \cdot & \cdot \\
\cdot & \cdot & \cdot & \cdot & \cdot & \cdot & & & \\
 & & b_0 & b_1 & \cdot & \cdot & \cdot & b_m &
\end{vmatrix}
\begin{array}{l} \left.\rule{0pt}{40pt}\right\} m \text{ rows} \\ \left.\rule{0pt}{40pt}\right\} n \text{ rows} \end{array}
$$

the blank spaces consisting of zeros. It will be observed that the determinant $\mathcal{R}(f, g)$ may be obtained by simply interchanging the rows and columns of the determinant of the coefficients of the unknowns in the equations (65). We have therefore established the following result:

THEOREM 55. *If $f(\lambda)$ is a monic polynomial of positive degree, the nonzero element $g(\lambda)$ of $R[\lambda]$ is related to the ideal $(f(\lambda))$ if and only if $\Re(f, g)$ is a divisor of zero in R.*

We have already shown in Theorem 52 that there exists a matrix A of R_n whose characteristic polynomial is any given monic polynomial of degree n. The following theorem indicates how the notion of resultant is connected with the theory of matrices.

THEOREM 56. *If $A = \| a_{ij} \|$ is an element of R_n with characteristic polynomial $f(\lambda)$, and $g(\lambda)$ is any nonzero element of $R[\lambda]$, then*

$$\Re(f, g) = | g(A) |.$$

If $g(\lambda)$ is a nonzero element b of R, it is easily verified directly that $\Re(f, g) = b^n = | g(A) |$; hence we assume that $g(\lambda)$ has positive degree m.

The method of proof of this theorem is essentially that used in showing that the usual determinant expansion theorems are valid if the elements are in the ring R. That is, we first prove the theorem for the case in which R is specialized to be the ring I of integers, and then use Theorem 11 to carry the result over to our general case. Accordingly, we now assume that A has elements in I, and that $g(\lambda)$ has coefficients in I. It is obvious that the characteristic polynomial $f(\lambda)$ of A then has coefficients in I. Let $f(\lambda)$ and $g(\lambda)$ be given by (59) and (60) respectively. Now I is a subring of the field of rational numbers and, by Theorem 21, this field may be extended to a field F such that in $F[\lambda]$ the polynomial $f(\lambda)g(\lambda)$ factors into linear factors. Hence in $F[\lambda]$, we have

$$(67) \qquad f(\lambda) = (\lambda - \lambda_1)(\lambda - \lambda_2) \cdots (\lambda - \lambda_n)$$

and

(68) $g(\lambda) = b_0(\lambda - \alpha_1)(\lambda - \alpha_2) \cdots (\lambda - \alpha_m).$

LEMMA. *If, in $F[\lambda]$, $f(\lambda)$ and $g(\lambda)$ have the factored forms* (67) *and* (68) *respectively, then*

$$|g(A)| = g(\lambda_1)g(\lambda_2) \cdots g(\lambda_n).$$

To prove this, we see from (68) that

$$g(A) = (-1)^m b_0(\alpha_1 - A)(\alpha_2 - A) \cdots (\alpha_m - A),$$

and thus

$$|g(A)| = (-1)^{mn} b_0^n |\alpha_1 - A| \cdot |\alpha_2 - A| \cdots |\alpha_m - A|.$$

But $|\lambda - A| = f(\lambda)$, hence it follows that

$$|g(A)| = (-1)^{mn} b_0^n f(\alpha_1)f(\alpha_2)\cdots f(\alpha_m)$$

$$= (-1)^{mn} b_0^n \prod (\alpha_i - \lambda_j),$$

where i takes the values $1, 2, \cdots, m$; and j independently the values $1, 2, \cdots, n$. Hence we may write

$$|g(A)| = b_0^n \prod (\lambda_j - \alpha_i) = g(\lambda_1)g(\lambda_2)\cdots g(\lambda_n),$$

which proves the lemma.

Now a familiar formula from the theory of equations[*] states that also

$$\mathcal{R}(f, g) = g(\lambda_1)g(\lambda_2) \cdots g(\lambda_n).$$

The theorem is therefore established in the restricted case under discussion.

We now let x_{ij} $(i, j = 1, 2, \cdots, n), y_k$ $(k = 0, 1, \cdots, m)$ be indeterminates and consider the ring $I' = I[x_{11}, \cdots, x_{nn}, y_0, \cdots, y_m]$. Let $A' = \|x_{ij}\|$ and define the element $g'(\lambda)$ of $I'[\lambda]$ by

[*] See, e.g., L. E. Dickson, *Elementary Theory of Equations*, Wiley and Sons, 1914, §2 and §9 of Chap. XII.

$$g'(\lambda) = y_0 \lambda^m + y_1 \lambda^{m-1} + \cdots + y_m .$$

If the characteristic polynomial of A' is $f'(\lambda)$, it is clear that $f'(\lambda)$ has coefficients in I'. Thus $\mathcal{R}(f', g')$ and $|\, g'(A')\, |$ are elements of I' which we may indicate by writing

$$\mathcal{R}(f', g') = F(x_{11}, \cdots, x_{nn}, y_0, \cdots, y_m),$$

and

$$|\, g'(A')\, | = G(x_{11}, \cdots, x_{nn}, y_0, \cdots, y_m).$$

By the case already established we know that F and G become equal elements of I under any substitution of integers for the indeterminates, so long as y_0 is replaced by a nonzero integer which will assure us that $g(\lambda)$ has degree m. In particular, this will be true if all the indeterminates are replaced by any positive integers. It follows from Theorem 11 that

$$F(a_{11}, \cdots, a_{nn}, b_0, \cdots, b_m) = G(a_{11}, \cdots, a_{nn}, b_0, \\ \cdots, b_m),$$

where a_{ij} $(i, j = 1, 2, \cdots, n)$, b_k $(k = 0, 1, \cdots, m)$ are elements of the arbitrary commutative ring R with unit element. If $A = \|\, a_{ij}\, \|$ has characteristic polynomial $f(\lambda)$ given by (59), and $g(\lambda)$ is defined by (60), this merely states that

$$\mathcal{R}(f, g) = |\, g(A)\, |,$$

and the theorem is therefore established.

As a simple example in which the main results of this section may be easily verified directly, let us again consider the matrix

$$A^* = \begin{bmatrix} 3' & 6' \\ 0' & 9' \end{bmatrix}$$

with elements in the ring $I/(12)$, which has been used above. For this matrix, the characteristic polynomial is $f(\lambda) = \lambda^2 + 3'$, and let us take $g(\lambda) = 2'\lambda + 5'$. Then

$$\mathcal{R}(f, g) = \begin{vmatrix} 1' & 0' & 3' \\ 2' & 5' & 0' \\ 0' & 2' & 5' \end{vmatrix} = 1',$$

and an easy calculation shows that

$$g(A^*) = \begin{bmatrix} 11' & 0' \\ 0' & 11' \end{bmatrix},$$

and hence $|g(A^*)| = 1'$ also. Incidentally, since $\mathcal{R}(f, g)$ is not a divisor of zero in $I/(12)$, it follows from Theorem 55 that $g(\lambda)$ is unrelated to $(\lambda^2 + 3')$, a fact which may also be verified directly by showing that if

$$(2'\lambda + 5')(a\lambda + b) = c(\lambda^2 + 3'),$$

where a, b, c are elements of $I/(12)$, then $a = b = c = 0$.

On the other hand, if we take $g(\lambda) = 2'\lambda + 3'$, then $\mathcal{R}(f, g) = |g(A^*)| = 9'$, which is a divisor of zero. Hence $g(\lambda)$ is related to $\lambda^2 + 3'$. In fact, it is easy to see that

$$(2'\lambda + 3')4'\lambda = 8'(\lambda^2 + 3'),$$

and clearly $4'\lambda$ is not in the ideal $(\lambda^2 + 3')$.

40. **Divisors of zero.** We have already obtained, in the Corollary to Theorem 51, a necessary and sufficient condition that an element A of R_n be a divisor of zero, namely, that $|A|$ be a divisor of zero in R. Now A is clearly an element of the subring $R[A]$ of R_n whose elements are expressible as polynomials in A with coefficients from R. We shall now prove

THEOREM 57. *The element A of R_n is a divisor of zero in R_n if and only if it is a divisor of zero in $R[A]$.*

Since $R[A]$ is a subring of R_n, the sufficiency of the condition is obvious. Also, in view of the Corollary to Theorem 51, we only need to prove that if $|A|$ is a divisor of zero in R, then there is a nonzero element $g(A)$ of $R[A]$ such that $Ag(A) = 0$. We shall presently do this but first we need the following

LEMMA. *If C and D are elements of R_n, and b an element of R such that $bC = bD$, then $b|C| = b|D|$.*

We shall illustrate the proof for the case in which $n = 3$ but it will be obvious that the method is applicable in general. If $C = \|c_{ij}\|$, $D = \|d_{ij}\|$, then our hypothesis is that for all i, j, we have $bc_{ij} = bd_{ij}$. It follows therefore that

$$b|C| = \begin{vmatrix} bc_{11} & bc_{12} & bc_{13} \\ c_{21} & c_{22} & c_{23} \\ c_{31} & c_{32} & c_{33} \end{vmatrix} = \begin{vmatrix} bd_{11} & bd_{12} & bd_{13} \\ c_{21} & c_{22} & c_{23} \\ c_{31} & c_{32} & c_{33} \end{vmatrix}$$

$$= b\begin{vmatrix} d_{11} & d_{12} & d_{13} \\ c_{21} & c_{22} & c_{23} \\ c_{31} & c_{32} & c_{33} \end{vmatrix} = \begin{vmatrix} d_{11} & d_{12} & d_{13} \\ bc_{21} & bc_{22} & bc_{23} \\ c_{31} & c_{32} & c_{33} \end{vmatrix}$$

$$= \begin{vmatrix} d_{11} & d_{12} & d_{13} \\ bd_{21} & bd_{22} & bd_{23} \\ c_{31} & c_{32} & c_{33} \end{vmatrix} = \begin{vmatrix} d_{11} & d_{12} & d_{13} \\ d_{21} & d_{22} & d_{23} \\ bc_{31} & bc_{32} & bc_{33} \end{vmatrix}$$

$$= \begin{vmatrix} d_{11} & d_{12} & d_{13} \\ d_{21} & d_{22} & d_{23} \\ bd_{31} & bd_{32} & bd_{33} \end{vmatrix} = b|D|.$$

We return to the proof of the theorem and assume that $|A|$ is a divisor of zero in R. In order to illustrate the general inductive process involved we shall suppose that $n > 2$. If

$$f(\lambda) = \lambda^n + a_1\lambda^{n-1} + \cdots + a_n$$

is the characteristic polynomial of A, then a_n is a divisor of zero since $a_n = (-1)^n |A|$, and hence there exists a nonzero element b of R such that $ba_n = 0$. Then, since $f(A) = 0$, it follows that

$$bA(A^{n-1} + \cdots + a_{n-1}) = 0.$$

If $b(A^{n-1} + \cdots + a_{n-1}) \neq 0$, this shows that A is a divisor of zero in $R[A]$, and the proof is completed. Hence assume that

$$(69) \qquad b(A^{n-1} + \cdots + a_{n-1}) = 0,$$

which we write in the form

$$bA(A^{n-2} + \cdots + a_{n-2}) = -ba_{n-1}.$$

An application of the Lemma shows that

$$b|A| \cdot |A^{n-2} + \cdots + a_{n-2}| = b(-1)^n a_{n-1}^n,$$

and, since $b|A| = 0$, we must have $ba_{n-1}^n = 0$. Let i be the least positive integer such that $ba_{n-1}^i = 0$, and set $b' = ba_{n-1}^{i-1}$ if $i > 1$, and $b' = b$ if $i = 1$. Thus $b' \neq 0$, $b'a_n = b'a_{n-1} = 0$, and we see from equation (69) that

$$b'A(A^{n-2} + \cdots + a_{n-2}) = 0.$$

If $b'(A^{n-2} + \cdots + a_{n-2}) \neq 0$, then A is a divisor of zero in $R[A]$, and hence we only need to consider the case in which

$$(70) \qquad b'(A^{n-2} + \cdots + a_{n-2}) = 0.$$

Now a repetition of the argument by which we passed from equation (69) to equation (70) will finally show that either A is a divisor of zero in $R[A]$ or there exists a non-zero element b^* of R such that $b^*A = 0$. However, $R[A]$ contains b^* since it contains all scalar matrices, and thus A must be a divisor of zero in $R[A]$.

COROLLARY. *An element $g(A)$ of $R[A]$ is a divisor of zero in R_n if and only if it is a divisor of zero in $R[A]$.*

If $g(A)$ is a divisor of zero in R_n it is a divisor of zero in $R[g(A)]$, a subring of $R[A]$, and hence is a divisor of zero in $R[A]$.

We shall now prove

THEOREM 58. *An element $g(\lambda)$ of $R[\lambda]$ is related to the null ideal $\mathfrak{n}$ of a matrix A if and only if it is related to the characteristic ideal of A.*

We recall that, by definition, $g(\lambda)$ is related to $\mathfrak{n}$ if and only if there is a polynomial $h(\lambda)$ not in $\mathfrak{n}$ such that $g(\lambda)h(\lambda) \equiv 0(\mathfrak{n})$, and this is true if and only if $g(A)$ is a divisor of zero in $R[A]$. By the result just proved and the Corollary to Theorem 51, $g(A)$ is a divisor of zero in $R[A]$ if and only if $|g(A)|$ is a divisor of zero in R. The desired result then follows at once from Theorems 55 and 56.

Corollary 2 to Theorem 54 shows that the minimal prime ideals belonging to the null ideal of a matrix coincide with the minimal prime ideals belonging to the characteristic ideal. We may supplement this by the following immediate consequence of the preceding theorem:

COROLLARY. *The maximal prime ideals belonging to the null ideal of a matrix A coincide with the maximal prime ideals belonging to the characteristic ideal of A.*

For the theory of matrices, generally with elements in a field or integral domain, see Albert [1], Chapters III, IV, V; [2], Chapters II, III, IV, V; Birkhoff and MacLane [1], Chapters VIII, IX; Dickson [2], Chapters III, IV, V, VI; Halmos [1]; MacDuffee [1]; [2], Chapter VII; [3]; van der Waerden [1], Chapter XV; Wedderburn [2].

The material of the present chapter is based primarily on results to be found in McCoy [2], [3], [4].

CHAPTER IX

FURTHER THEORY OF IDEALS IN COMMUTATIVE RINGS

41. Primary ideals. Throughout this chapter we shall consider *commutative* rings only.

It was pointed out in Chapter V that in some important respects the prime ideals in an arbitrary commutative ring play a role similar to that of the primes in the ring I of integers. We now study a more general class of ideals which will be seen to bear roughly the same relation to the *powers* of a prime integer that the prime ideals do to the primes themselves.

An ideal q in the commutative ring R is said to be *primary* if $ab \equiv 0(q)$, $a \not\equiv 0(q)$, imply that $b^i \equiv 0(q)$ for some positive integer i. As a simple illustration, it is clear that in the ring I every ideal (p^n), where p is a prime and n a positive integer, is primary. Furthermore, R is always a primary ideal, and (0) is primary if and only if every divisor of zero in R is nilpotent. Any prime ideal is also primary, and thus the concept of primary ideal may be considered as a natural generalization of that of prime ideal.

A primary ideal may just as well be defined as an ideal q with the property that if $ab \equiv 0(q)$ and $b^k \not\equiv 0(q)$ for *all* positive integers k, then $a \equiv 0(q)$. This form of the definition will sometimes be useful in proving that a given ideal is primary. It may also be verified that a primary ideal can be characterized as an ideal q such that in the residue class ring R/q every divisor of zero is nilpotent.

In the following and later sections, the role of the primary ideals will be made more clear, but we now give additional examples and prove a few simple properties.

Let us consider the ideal $q_1 = (x^2, xy, y^2)$ in the ring $I[x, y]$ of polynomials in the indeterminates x and y, with integral coefficients. The nonzero elements of this ideal are precisely the polynomials which are expressible as a sum of terms of degree ≥ 2. If, therefore, $fg \equiv 0(q_1)$, $f \not\equiv 0(q_1)$, it follows that the constant term in g must be zero and hence $g^2 \equiv 0(q_1)$. This shows that q_1 is a primary ideal.

The ideal $q_2 = (x^2, y)$ in $I[x, y]$ is also primary, as we proceed to show. If f is any element of $I[x, y]$ it is easy to see that

$$f \equiv a + bx \ (q_2),$$

where a and b are integers; and $f \equiv 0(q_2)$ if and only if $a = b = 0$. Suppose now that $fg \equiv 0(q_2), f \not\equiv 0(q_2)$, where

$$g \equiv c + dx \ (q_2).$$

Thus

$$fg \equiv ac + (ad + bc)x \equiv 0(q_2),$$

and we must have $ac = 0$, $ad + bc = 0$. Since not both a and b are zero, it follows that $c = 0$ and hence $g^2 \equiv 0(q_2)$, that is, q_2 is primary.

It will be recalled that the *radical* of an ideal a is the ideal consisting of all elements a of R such that $a^j \equiv 0(a)$ for some positive integer j. We now show that *the radical of a primary ideal is a prime ideal*. Let q be a primary ideal with radical r and suppose that $ab \equiv 0(r)$, $a \not\equiv 0(r)$. No integral power of a is in q but $(ab)^j = a^j b^j \equiv 0(q)$ for some positive integer j. Since $a^j \not\equiv 0(q)$, it follows that $(b^j)^i \equiv 0(q)$; hence $b \equiv 0(r)$, and r is therefore a prime ideal.

It was pointed out in §21 that an ideal and its radical are contained in precisely the same prime ideals. From this, it follows that *the radical* $\mathfrak{p}$ *of a primary ideal* $\mathfrak{q}$ *is the only minimal prime ideal belonging to* $\mathfrak{q}$. We now show that *the radical* $\mathfrak{p}$ *of a primary ideal* $\mathfrak{q} \neq R$ *is the only maximal prime ideal belonging to* $\mathfrak{q}$. In view of Theorem 27, we only need to show that any element a not in $\mathfrak{p}$ is unrelated to $\mathfrak{q}$. Suppose that $a \not\equiv 0(\mathfrak{p})$, $ax \equiv 0(\mathfrak{q})$. Since no power of a is in $\mathfrak{q}$, it follows from the definition of primary ideal that $x \equiv 0(\mathfrak{q})$, and therefore a is unrelated to $\mathfrak{q}$.

In view of the fact that the radical $\mathfrak{p}$ of a primary ideal $\mathfrak{q} \neq R$ is the unique minimal and maximal prime ideal belonging to $\mathfrak{q}$, we shall say that $\mathfrak{p}$ is *the prime ideal belonging to* $\mathfrak{q}$. It is obvious that $\mathfrak{p}$, being the radical of $\mathfrak{q}$, is uniquely determined by $\mathfrak{q}$, and that $\mathfrak{q} \subseteq \mathfrak{p}$. However $\mathfrak{q}$ need not be uniquely determined by $\mathfrak{p}$ as is easily shown by examples. Thus, in the ring of integers, it is obvious that the prime ideal (p) is the prime ideal belonging to the primary ideal (p^j), for any positive integer j. Also, in the ring $I[x, y]$ it is readily verified that the prime ideal (x, y) is the prime ideal belonging to both of the primary ideals (x^2, xy, y^2) and (x^2, y) mentioned above.

We now point out that the entire ring R may be the prime ideal belonging to a primary ideal $\mathfrak{q} \neq R$. As a simple example, this is the case if R is the subring of $I/(8)$ consisting of the elements $0', 2', 4', 6'$; and $\mathfrak{q}$ is the primary ideal with elements $0', 4'$.

The following theorem furnishes a useful characterization of the primary ideals.

THEOREM 59. *An ideal* $\mathfrak{q} \neq R$ *is a primary ideal if and only if there exists a prime ideal* $\mathfrak{p}$ *which is the unique minimal prime ideal belonging to* $\mathfrak{q}$ *and the unique maximal prime ideal belonging to* $\mathfrak{q}$.

In view of the remarks made above we only need to show that if the prime ideal $\mathfrak{p}$ is the unique minimal and maximal prime ideal belonging to $\mathfrak{q}$, then $\mathfrak{q}$ is primary.

Suppose, therefore, that $ab \equiv 0(\mathfrak{q})$ and that $a^i \not\equiv 0(\mathfrak{q})$ for all positive integers i. Thus a is not in the radical of $\mathfrak{q}$ which, by Theorem 24, is precisely $\mathfrak{p}$. Theorem 26 then shows that a is unrelated to $\mathfrak{q}$ and therefore $ab \equiv 0(\mathfrak{q})$ implies that $b \equiv 0(\mathfrak{q})$. Hence $\mathfrak{q}$ is a primary ideal as required.

42. **The intersection of primary ideals.** If n is a positive integer and

$$n = p_1^{\alpha_1} p_2^{\alpha_2} \cdots p_k^{\alpha_k},$$

where the p_i are the distinct prime factors of n, then an integer m is divisible by n if and only if m is divisible by all $p_i^{\alpha_i}$ $(i = 1, 2, \cdots, k)$. Otherwise expressed, the ideal (n) is the intersection of the primary ideals $(p_i^{\alpha_i})$, $i = 1$, $2, \cdots, k$. Although it is not true in all rings, there are important classes of rings (see §45) in which *every* ideal can be represented as the intersection of a finite number of primary ideals. In this and the next two sections we shall develop some properties of any ideal which can be so represented.

If $\mathfrak{b}_1$, $\mathfrak{b}_2$, $\cdots$, $\mathfrak{b}_k$ are ideals in the ring R, we denote their intersection by the notation

$$\mathfrak{b}_1 \cap \mathfrak{b}_2 \cap \cdots \cap \mathfrak{b}_k.$$

If, for example,

$$\mathfrak{b}_2 \cap \mathfrak{b}_3 \cap \cdots \cap \mathfrak{b}_k \subseteq \mathfrak{b}_1,$$

then it is clear that $\mathfrak{b}_1$ may be omitted, that is, that

$$\mathfrak{b}_1 \cap \mathfrak{b}_2 \cap \cdots \cap \mathfrak{b}_k = \mathfrak{b}_2 \cap \mathfrak{b}_3 \cap \cdots \cap \mathfrak{b}_k.$$

We now consider an ideal

(71) $$\mathfrak{a} = \mathfrak{q}_1 \cap \mathfrak{q}_2 \cap \cdots \cap \mathfrak{q}_r,$$

where the $\mathfrak{q}_i$ are primary ideals. If no one of the $\mathfrak{q}_i$ contains the intersection of the remaining ones, then none of the q's can be omitted in (71) and we may call (71) an *irre-dundant* representation of $\mathfrak{a}$ as the intersection of primary ideals. It is clear that if an ideal can be represented as the intersection of a finite number of primary ideals, either this representation is irredundant or from it one can obtain an irredundant representation by the simple process of successively striking out ideals which contain the intersection of the remaining ones.

Before proceeding, we point out the important fact that in an irredundant representation of an ideal as the intersection of primary ideals, the primary ideals are not necessarily unique. For example, in the ring $I[x, y]$, we shall show that

(72) $(x^2, xy) = (x^2, xy, y^2) \cap (x),$

and also

(73) $(x^2, xy) = (x^2, y) \cap (x).$

It was proved in §41 that (x^2, xy, y^2) and (x^2, y) are primary ideals, while (x) is a prime ideal, as shown in §20, and therefore also primary. When we have established the relations (72) and (73) we will have therefore shown that the ideal (x^2, xy) has two different (obviously irredundant) representations as the intersection of primary ideals.

We observe first that the nonzero elements of (x^2, xy) are the polynomials of degree ≥ 2 which have x as a factor. The nonzero elements of (x^2, xy, y^2) are the polynomials of degree ≥ 2. Thus the nonzero elements of $(x^2, xy, y^2) \cap (x)$ are the polynomials of degree ≥ 2 which have x as a factor, that is, they are the nonzero elements of (x^2, xy). To prove relation (73), we note that (x^2, y) consists of the polynomials in which both the constant term and the coefficient of x are zero. Thus $(x^2, y) \cap (x)$ consists of the polynomials which have x as a factor and in which the coefficient of x is zero. However, these are precisely the zero polynomial together with those polynomials of degree ≥ 2 which have x as a factor, in other words, the elements of (x^2, xy).

We now assume that $\mathfrak{a}$ is an ideal with the *irredundant representation*

$$(74) \qquad \mathfrak{a} = \mathfrak{q}_1 \cap \mathfrak{q}_2 \cap \cdots \cap \mathfrak{q}_k$$

as the intersection of primary ideals $\mathfrak{q}_i$, and that $\mathfrak{p}_i$ is the prime ideal belonging to $\mathfrak{q}_i$ ($i = 1, 2, \cdots, k$). We henceforth tacitly exclude the trivial case in which $\mathfrak{a} = R$ and thus, since (74) is an irredundant representation, no one of the primary ideals $\mathfrak{q}_i$ can be R. It is clear that, for each i, $\mathfrak{a} \subseteq \mathfrak{q}_i \subseteq \mathfrak{p}_i$.

If $\mathfrak{p}_l$ is properly contained in no $\mathfrak{p}_i$ ($i = 1, 2, \cdots, k$), then, in accordance with previous usage, $\mathfrak{p}_l$ may be said to be *maximal in the set* $\{\mathfrak{p}_i\}$ of prime ideals. Likewise $\mathfrak{p}_l$ is *minimal in this set* if no $\mathfrak{p}_i$ ($i = 1, 2, \cdots, k$) is properly contained in $\mathfrak{p}_l$.

THEOREM 60. *If (74) is an irredundant representation of the ideal $\mathfrak{a}$ as the intersection of primary ideals $\mathfrak{q}_i$, and $\mathfrak{p}_i$ is the prime ideal belonging to $\mathfrak{q}_i$ ($i = 1, 2, \cdots, k$), the minimal prime ideals belonging to $\mathfrak{a}$ are the prime ideals which are minimal in the set $\{\mathfrak{p}_i\}$, and the maximal prime ideals belonging to $\mathfrak{a}$ are the prime ideals which are maximal in the set $\{\mathfrak{p}_i\}$.*

The first statement of the theorem follows at once from

LEMMA 1. *If $\mathfrak{p}$ is a prime ideal such that $\mathfrak{a} \subseteq \mathfrak{p}$, then for at least one i, $\mathfrak{p}_i \subseteq \mathfrak{p}$.*

We shall prove this by showing that if $\mathfrak{p}$ is a prime ideal which contains no $\mathfrak{p}_i$ ($i = 1, 2, \cdots, k$), then there is an element of $\mathfrak{a}$ not in $\mathfrak{p}$. Since $\mathfrak{p}$ does not contain $\mathfrak{p}_i$ there is an element b_i of $\mathfrak{p}_i$ which is not in $\mathfrak{p}$, and for some positive integer n_i, $b_i^{n_i} \equiv 0(\mathfrak{q}_i)$. If we set

$$c = b_1^{n_1} b_2^{n_2} \cdots b_k^{n_k},$$

it is clear that c is in every $\mathfrak{q}_i$ and therefore in $\mathfrak{a}$. Furthermore, $c \not\equiv 0(\mathfrak{p})$ since no b_i is in the prime ideal $\mathfrak{p}$.

Before proving the second statement of the theorem we shall establish two additional lemmas.

LEMMA 2. *An element a of R is related to $\mathfrak{a}$ if and only if it is in the union of the prime ideals $\mathfrak{p}_i$ ($i = 1, 2, \cdots, k$).*

First, suppose that a is related to $\mathfrak{a}$ and that $ab \equiv 0(\mathfrak{a})$ with $b \not\equiv 0(\mathfrak{a})$. Then b is not in all $\mathfrak{q}_i$, as otherwise it would be in $\mathfrak{a}$; hence suppose that $b \not\equiv 0(\mathfrak{q}_1)$. Thus, since $\mathfrak{a} \subseteq \mathfrak{q}_1$, we have $ab \equiv 0(\mathfrak{q}_1)$, $b \not\equiv 0(\mathfrak{q}_1)$, and this implies that a is in the radical $\mathfrak{p}_1$ of $\mathfrak{q}_1$.

Conversely, let a be in the union of the $\mathfrak{p}_i$ ($i = 1, 2, \cdots, k$), and for convenience suppose that $a \equiv 0(\mathfrak{p}_1)$ and hence $a^j \equiv 0(\mathfrak{q}_1)$ for some positive integer j. Since the assumed representation (74) of $\mathfrak{a}$ is irredundant, there exists an element b of $\mathfrak{q}_2 \cap \mathfrak{q}_3 \cap \cdots \cap \mathfrak{q}_k$ which is not in $\mathfrak{q}_1$, and clearly $a^j b \equiv 0(\mathfrak{a})$, $b \not\equiv 0(\mathfrak{a})$. Let j_1 be the smallest positive integer such that $a^{j_1} b \equiv 0(\mathfrak{a})$, and set $c = b$ if $j_1 = 1$, and $c = a^{j_1 - 1} b$ if $j_1 > 1$. In either case $ac \equiv 0(\mathfrak{a})$, $c \not\equiv 0(\mathfrak{a})$, and a is therefore related to $\mathfrak{a}$.

LEMMA 3. *If an ideal $\mathfrak{b}$ is contained in the union of the prime ideals $\mathfrak{p}_i$ ($i = 1, 2, \cdots, k$), then $\mathfrak{b} \subseteq \mathfrak{p}_i$ for some i.*

The proof is by induction on k. The desired result is obvious if $k = 1$; we therefore assume the result for fewer than k prime ideals. Suppose that $\mathfrak{b}$ is not in the union of any $k - 1$ of the prime ideals $\mathfrak{p}_i$ ($i = 1, 2, \cdots, k$). Then, for each j, there exists an element b_j of $\mathfrak{b}$ which is in $\mathfrak{p}_j$ but not in any $\mathfrak{p}_i$ for $i \neq j$. Now

$$b_2 b_3 \cdots b_k + b_1 b_3 \cdots b_k + \cdots + b_1 b_2 \cdots b_{k-1}$$

is an element of $\mathfrak{b}$ and therefore is in some $\mathfrak{p}_i$, say $\mathfrak{p}_1$. It follows that $b_2 b_3 \cdots b_k \equiv 0(\mathfrak{p}_1)$ which is impossible since no one of the factors is in the prime ideal $\mathfrak{p}_1$. Hence $\mathfrak{b}$ is in the union of some $k - 1$ of the prime ideals $\mathfrak{p}_i$ $(i = 1, 2, \cdots, k)$ and, by the hypothesis of the induction, must therefore be contained in some $\mathfrak{p}_i$.

It is now easy to complete the proof of the theorem. By Lemma 2, the ideals $\mathfrak{p}_i$ are related to $\mathfrak{a}$ and, by Lemmas 2 and 3, any ideal related to $\mathfrak{a}$ is contained in some one of the $\mathfrak{p}_i$. Hence the maximal prime ideals belonging to $\mathfrak{a}$ are just the prime ideals which are maximal in the set $\{\mathfrak{p}_i\}$.

Theorem 60 shows that in a representation (74), the prime ideals which are minimal or maximal in the set $\{\mathfrak{p}_i\}$ can be characterized in terms of the properties of $\mathfrak{a}$ itself, independent of its representation, and therefore are the same in *all* irredundant representations of $\mathfrak{a}$. In the following section we shall likewise give an intrinsic characterization of all the different prime ideals $\mathfrak{p}_i$.

43. **The prime ideals belonging to** $\mathfrak{a}$. If $\mathfrak{p} \neq R$ is any prime ideal, not necessarily one of the $\mathfrak{p}_i$, let us denote by $\mathfrak{a}(\mathfrak{p})$ the set of all elements b of R such that $bs \equiv 0(\mathfrak{a})$ for some element s not in $\mathfrak{p}$. First we observe that $\mathfrak{a}(\mathfrak{p})$ is an ideal. For if $bs_1 \equiv 0(\mathfrak{a})$, $cs_2 \equiv 0(\mathfrak{a})$, where s_1 and s_2 are not in $\mathfrak{p}$, then $(b - c)s_1 s_2 \equiv 0(\mathfrak{a})$, and $s_1 s_2 \not\equiv 0(\mathfrak{p})$ since $\mathfrak{p}$ is a prime ideal. Hence $b - c$ is in $\mathfrak{a}(\mathfrak{p})$ if b and c are in $\mathfrak{a}(\mathfrak{p})$. Furthermore, if $bs \equiv 0(\mathfrak{a})$ then $brs \equiv 0(\mathfrak{a})$ for any element r of R, so that br is in $\mathfrak{a}(\mathfrak{p})$ if b is. Thus $\mathfrak{a}(\mathfrak{p})$ is an ideal which depends on the ideals $\mathfrak{a}$ and $\mathfrak{p}$, and it is clear that $\mathfrak{a} \subseteq \mathfrak{a}(\mathfrak{p})$.

We now prove the following

LEMMA. *Let* $\mathfrak{a}$ *have the irredundant representation* (74) *as the intersection of the primary ideals* $\mathfrak{q}_i$ $(i = 1, 2, \cdots, k)$.

If $\mathfrak{p} \neq R$ is a prime ideal which contains $\mathfrak{p}_1$, $\mathfrak{p}_2$, $\cdots$, $\mathfrak{p}_r$ ($1 \leq r \leq k$) but does not contain $\mathfrak{p}_{r+1}$, $\cdots$, $\mathfrak{p}_k$, then

$$(75) \qquad \mathfrak{a}(\mathfrak{p}) = \mathfrak{q}_1 \cap \mathfrak{q}_2 \cap \cdots \cap \mathfrak{q}_r .$$

If $\mathfrak{p}$ contains none of the $\mathfrak{p}_i$, then $\mathfrak{a}(\mathfrak{p}) = R$.

We first assume that $\mathfrak{p}$ contains $\mathfrak{p}_1$, $\mathfrak{p}_2$, $\cdots$, $\mathfrak{p}_r$; and let b be any element of $\mathfrak{a}(\mathfrak{p})$. Then, for some $s \not\equiv 0(\mathfrak{p})$, we have $bs \equiv 0(\mathfrak{a})$, and thus

$$bs \equiv 0(\mathfrak{q}_i) \qquad (i = 1, 2, \cdots, k).$$

However, s is not in any $\mathfrak{p}_i$ ($i = 1, 2, \cdots, r$), and is therefore unrelated to $\mathfrak{q}_i$ ($i = 1, 2, \cdots, r$). Hence

$$b \equiv 0(\mathfrak{q}_i) \qquad (i = 1, 2, \cdots, r),$$

and thus

$$\mathfrak{a}(\mathfrak{p}) \subseteq \mathfrak{q}_1 \cap \mathfrak{q}_2 \cap \cdots \cap \mathfrak{q}_r .$$

We complete the proof of equation (75) by showing that

$$\mathfrak{q}_1 \cap \mathfrak{q}_2 \cap \cdots \cap \mathfrak{q}_r \subseteq \mathfrak{a}(\mathfrak{p}).$$

If $r = k$, this is trivial in view of the fact that $\mathfrak{a} \subseteq \mathfrak{a}(\mathfrak{p})$. Hence suppose that $r < k$ and let c be any element of $\mathfrak{q}_1 \cap \mathfrak{q}_2 \cap \cdots \cap \mathfrak{q}_r$. Since, for $i = r + 1, \cdots, k$, $\mathfrak{p}_i$ contains an element p_i not in $\mathfrak{p}$, we must have for suitably chosen positive integers α_i,

$$p_i^{\alpha_i} \equiv 0(\mathfrak{q}_i) \qquad (i = r + 1, \cdots, k).$$

If we set

$$t = p_{r+1}^{\alpha_{r+1}} \cdots p_k^{\alpha_k},$$

then $t \not\equiv 0(\mathfrak{p})$ and

$$t \equiv 0(\mathfrak{q}_{r+1} \cap \cdots \cap \mathfrak{q}_k).$$

Since c is in $\mathfrak{q}_1 \cap \mathfrak{q}_2 \cap \cdots \cap \mathfrak{q}_r$, it follows that

$$ct \equiv 0(\mathfrak{a}),$$

and thus c is in $\mathfrak{a}(\mathfrak{p})$.

If $\mathfrak{p}$ contains none of the $\mathfrak{p}_i$, then the last part of the above proof shows that there is an element

$$d = p_1^{\alpha_1} p_2^{\alpha_2} \cdots p_k^{\alpha_k}$$

of $\mathfrak{a}$ which is not in $\mathfrak{p}$. Hence $yd \equiv 0(\mathfrak{a})$ for *all* elements y of R, that is, $\mathfrak{a}(\mathfrak{p}) = R$. This completes the proof of the lemma.

We note that if $r \geq 1$, (75) is actually an irredundant representation of $\mathfrak{a}(\mathfrak{p})$ as the intersection of primary ideals. For if, say, $\mathfrak{q}_1$ contained $\mathfrak{q}_2 \cap \mathfrak{q}_3 \cap \cdots \cap \mathfrak{q}_r$, it would clearly contain $\mathfrak{q}_2 \cap \mathfrak{q}_3 \cap \cdots \cap \mathfrak{q}_k$, and this is impossible since (74) is assumed to be an irredundant representation of $\mathfrak{a}$.

We may now easily establish

THEOREM 61. *Let $\mathfrak{a}$ have the irredundant representation* (74) *as the intersection of the primary ideals* $\mathfrak{q}_i$ $(i = 1, 2, \cdots, k)$ *and let $\mathfrak{p}_i$ be the prime ideal belonging to $\mathfrak{q}_i$ $(i = 1, 2, \cdots, k)$. A prime ideal $\mathfrak{p} \neq R$ is one of the $\mathfrak{p}_i$ if and only if $\mathfrak{p}$ is a maximal prime ideal belonging to $\mathfrak{a}(\mathfrak{p})$. The ring R is one of the $\mathfrak{p}_i$ if and only if R is a maximal prime ideal belonging to $\mathfrak{a}$.*

The last sentence follows from Theorem 60; hence let $\mathfrak{p}$ be different from R. If $\mathfrak{p} = \mathfrak{p}_j$, then the Lemma shows that $\mathfrak{a}(\mathfrak{p}_j)$ has an irredundant representation as the intersection of certain of the primary ideals $\mathfrak{q}_i$, where $\mathfrak{p}_j$ is the prime ideal belonging to one of these primary ideals and contains all the prime ideals belonging to the others of this set. Thus, among the prime ideals belonging to the primary ideals of this set, $\mathfrak{p}_j$ is a maximal one. Hence, by Theorem 60, $\mathfrak{p}_j$ is a maximal prime ideal belonging to $\mathfrak{a}(\mathfrak{p}_j)$.

Conversely, suppose that $\mathfrak{p} \neq R$ is a maximal prime ideal belonging to $\mathfrak{a}(\mathfrak{p})$. We note first that $\mathfrak{p}$ must contain at least one $\mathfrak{p}_i$. For if this were not the case, the Lemma shows that $\mathfrak{a}(\mathfrak{p}) = R$ which is impossible since $\mathfrak{a}(\mathfrak{p}) \subseteq \mathfrak{p} \neq R$. If $\mathfrak{p}$ contains $\mathfrak{p}_1$, $\mathfrak{p}_2$, $\cdots$, $\mathfrak{p}_r$ but does not contain $\mathfrak{p}_{r+1}$, $\cdots$, $\mathfrak{p}_k$, then (75) is an irredundant representation of $\mathfrak{a}(\mathfrak{p})$ as the intersection of primary ideals, and Theorem 60 shows that $\mathfrak{p}$ is a maximal ideal in the set $\{\mathfrak{p}_1, \mathfrak{p}_2, \cdots, \mathfrak{p}_r\}$; and therefore one of the $\mathfrak{p}_i$ as required.

Now, by definition, $\mathfrak{a}(\mathfrak{p})$ depends only on the ideals $\mathfrak{a}$ and $\mathfrak{p}$, and not on any particular representation of $\mathfrak{a}$. Hence the last theorem shows that the different prime ideals $\mathfrak{p}_i$ can be characterized in terms of the ideal $\mathfrak{a}$ itself and are therefore the same in *any* irredundant representation of $\mathfrak{a}$ as the intersection of primary ideals. We naturally call these prime ideals the *prime ideals belonging to* $\mathfrak{a}$. It will be observed that our terminology is consistent in that, by Theorem 60, the maximal (minimal) prime ideals belonging to $\mathfrak{a}$ as defined in Chapter V are precisely the maximal (minimal) among the prime ideals belonging to $\mathfrak{a}$.

44. Short representation of an ideal. In a representation (74) of an ideal $\mathfrak{a}$ as the intersection of primary ideals $\mathfrak{q}_i$, it may happen that the prime ideals $\mathfrak{p}_i$ belonging to the different $\mathfrak{q}_i$ are not all different. It is therefore of interest to prove

THEOREM 62. *If $\mathfrak{p}$ is the prime ideal belonging to each of the primary ideals $\mathfrak{q}_1$, $\mathfrak{q}_2$, $\cdots$, $\mathfrak{q}_s$, then the ideal $\mathfrak{q}_1 \cap \mathfrak{q}_2 \cap \cdots \cap \mathfrak{q}_s$ is primary and $\mathfrak{p}$ is the prime ideal belonging to this primary ideal.*

If necessary, some of the $\mathfrak{q}_i$ may be omitted to form an irredundant representation of the ideal $\mathfrak{q}_1 \cap \mathfrak{q}_2 \cap \cdots \cap \mathfrak{q}_s$, so we may assume without loss of generality that it is already irredundant. Hence, by Theorem 60, $\mathfrak{p}$ is the unique minimal and maximal prime ideal belonging to $q_1 \cap q_2 \cap \cdots \cap q_s$, and the desired result is then an immediate consequence of Theorem 59.

We also have the related result:

THEOREM 63. *If the prime ideals* $\mathfrak{p}_i$ *belonging to the primary ideals* q_i $(i = 1, 2, \cdots, s)$ *do not all coincide, and* $q_1 \cap q_2 \cap \cdots \cap q_s$ *is irredundant, it is not primary.*

If there are at least two different $\mathfrak{p}_i$, there does not exist among the set of all $\mathfrak{p}_i$ a unique one which is both minimal and maximal. Theorems 60 and 59 then show that $q_1 \cap q_2 \cap \cdots \cap q_s$ is not primary.

Now let $\mathfrak{a}$ be an ideal which can be represented as the intersection of a finite number of primary ideals, say

$$\mathfrak{a} = q_1 \cap q_2 \cap \cdots \cap q_l .$$

If this representation is not irredundant it can be made so by omitting certain of the q_i, and suppose the notation is so chosen that

$$\mathfrak{a} = q_1 \cap q_2 \cap \cdots \cap q_k$$

is an irredundant representation of $\mathfrak{a}$ as the intersection of primary ideals. As usual, let us denote by $\mathfrak{p}_i$ the prime ideal belonging to q_i $(i = 1, 2, \cdots, k)$. If the $\mathfrak{p}_i$ are not all different, Theorem 62 shows that the intersection of certain of the q_i may be replaced by a single primary ideal. After making all possible replacements of this kind, we get the irredundant representation

$$(76) \qquad \mathfrak{a} = q_1' \cap q_2' \cap \cdots \cap q_n',$$

where the q_i' are primary and the prime ideals $\mathfrak{p}_i'$ belonging to the q_i' are all different. Furthermore, Theorem 63 shows that the intersection of no two or more of the q_i' is primary. Accordingly, we shall call (76) a *short* representation of $\mathfrak{a}$ as the intersection of primary ideals. Thus an irredundant representation of $\mathfrak{a}$ as the intersection of primary ideals is a short representation if and only if the prime ideals belonging to these primary ideals are all different.

In a short representation (76), Theorem 61 shows that the distinct prime ideals $\mathfrak{p}'_i$ $(i = 1, 2, \cdots, n)$ are all uniquely determined by $\mathfrak{a}$, independent of its representation. In particular, we have the following important result:

THEOREM 64. *Any ideal which can be represented as the intersection of a finite number of primary ideals has a short representation as the intersection of primary ideals. In all short representations of a given ideal the number of primary ideals is the same, and the set of prime ideals belonging to these primary ideals is the same.*

As an illustration of this theorem, it may be pointed out that both (72) and (73) are short representations of the ideal (x^2, xy) in $I[x, y]$. In each case, there are two primary ideals in the short representation, and the prime ideals belonging to these primary ideals are (x, y) and (x). It will be observed that the primary ideal (x) appears in both of the short representations (72) and (73). The next theorem will show why this is so.

Let $\{\mathfrak{q}'_{i_r}\}$ $(r = 1, 2, \cdots, m)$ be a set of one or more of the primary ideals occurring in a short representation (76) of $\mathfrak{a}$. The ideal

$$\mathfrak{b} = \mathfrak{q}'_{i_1} \cap \mathfrak{q}'_{i_2} \cap \cdots \cap \mathfrak{q}'_{i_m}$$

is said to be an *isolated component* of $\mathfrak{a}$ if no one of the prime ideals $\mathfrak{p}'_{i_r}$ $(r = 1, 2, \cdots, m)$ contains a prime ideal $\mathfrak{p}'_i$ belonging to $\mathfrak{a}$ which is not in this set. The lemma of §43 then shows that if $\mathfrak{p}'_{j_s}$ is a fixed ideal in this set, $\mathfrak{a}(\mathfrak{p}'_{j_s})$ can be expressed as the intersection of certain of the $\mathfrak{q}'_{i_r}$, one of which is certainly $\mathfrak{q}'_{i_s}$. It follows that

$$\mathfrak{b} = \mathfrak{a}(\mathfrak{p}'_{i_1}) \cap \mathfrak{a}(\mathfrak{p}'_{i_2}) \cap \cdots \cap \mathfrak{a}(\mathfrak{p}'_{i_m}),$$

and thus is uniquely determined by the prime ideals $\mathfrak{p}_{i_r}'$, $(r = 1, 2, \cdots, m)$. We have thus proved

THEOREM 65. *The prime ideals belonging to an isolated component of $\mathfrak{a}$ uniquely determine the isolated component. The isolated components of $\mathfrak{a}$ coincide in all short representations of $\mathfrak{a}$ as the intersection of primary ideals.*

A special case of this is of some interest. If $\mathfrak{q}_j'$ is a single primary ideal occurring in a short representation (76) of $\mathfrak{a}$, $\mathfrak{q}_j'$ is an *isolated primary component* of $\mathfrak{a}$ if $\mathfrak{p}_j'$ contains no $\mathfrak{p}_i'$ $(i \neq j)$. Thus, in view of Theorem 63, the isolated primary components of $\mathfrak{a}$ are just the isolated components which are primary. In particular, the last theorem shows that the isolated primary components of $\mathfrak{a}$ are the same in all short representations of $\mathfrak{a}$ as the intersection of primary ideals. In the example discussed above, the primary ideal (x) is an isolated primary component of (x^2, xy) since the prime ideal (x) does not contain the prime ideal (x, y). Hence (x) must appear in any short representation of (x^2, xy) as the intersection of primary ideals.

We next turn to the problem of characterizing a class of rings in which *every* ideal has a representation as the intersection of a finite number of primary ideals. In these rings, therefore, the results so far obtained are valid for any ideal.

45. Noetherian rings. A ring R is said to satisfy the *ascending chain condition* if each sequence of ideals $\mathfrak{a}_1, \mathfrak{a}_2, \cdots$ in R such that

$$\mathfrak{a}_1 \subset \mathfrak{a}_2 \subset \cdots$$

has only a finite number of terms. An equivalent, and frequently useful, formulation is that in each sequence of ideals $\mathfrak{a}_1, \mathfrak{a}_2, \cdots$ in R such that

$$\mathfrak{a}_1 \subseteq \mathfrak{a}_2 \subseteq \cdots,$$

the equality must hold from some point on.

Since a *field* has only the two trivial ideals, it is clear that a field satisfies the ascending chain condition. Also, in the ring I, $(n) \subset (m)$ implies that m is a divisor of n, and hence the condition is satisfied in I. Later on, we shall give other examples, but at this point it might be well to give an example of a ring which does not satisfy this condition. Let F be a field and consider polynomials in the infinite set of indeterminates, $x_1, x_2, \cdots$, with coefficients from F. Naturally, each single polynomial contains only a finite number of terms, and hence only a finite number of indeterminates can occur in any one polynomial. It is easy to see that the set of all such polynomials is a ring $F[x_1, x_2, \cdots]$, and in this ring we have the following infinite ascending chain of ideals:

$$(x_1) \subset (x_1, x_2) \subset (x_1, x_2, x_3) \subset \cdots.$$

Hence the ascending chain condition is not satisfied in this ring.

THEOREM 66. *For a commutative ring R the following are equivalent:*

(i) *R satisfies the ascending chain condition.*

(ii) *Every ideal in R has a finite basis.*

(iii) *Given any nonvoid set of ideals in R, there is at least one ideal which is maximal in this set.*

We first prove that (i) implies (ii). Let $\mathfrak{a}$ be an ideal in R, and a_1 an element of $\mathfrak{a}$. If $(a_1) = \mathfrak{a}$, $\mathfrak{a}$ has a basis of one element. If $(a_1) \subset \mathfrak{a}$, let a_2 be an element of $\mathfrak{a}$ which is not in (a_1), and hence

$$(a_1) \subset (a_1, a_2) \subseteq \mathfrak{a}.$$

If $(a_1, a_2) = \mathfrak{a}$, we have found a basis of two elements, while if $(a_1, a_2) \subset \mathfrak{a}$, we can repeat the above process and get

$$(a_1) \subset (a_1, a_2) \subset (a_1, a_2, a_3) \subseteq \mathfrak{a}.$$

In view of the ascending chain condition, this can not be repeated indefinitely and hence for some finite k we must have

$$\mathfrak{a} = (a_1, a_2, \cdots, a_k),$$

and $\mathfrak{a}$ has a finite basis of k elements.

We now assume (ii) and let $\mathfrak{A}$ be any set of ideals in R. If $\mathfrak{a}_1$ is any element of $\mathfrak{A}$, it is either a maximal element of $\mathfrak{A}$ or is properly contained in an element $\mathfrak{a}_2$ of $\mathfrak{A}$. Repeating this process, we either find a maximal element after a finite number of steps or get an infinite ascending chain

$$\mathfrak{a}_1 \subset \mathfrak{a}_2 \subset \cdots$$

of ideals in R. This is clearly a special type of linear system and hence the union of all the ideals $\mathfrak{a}_i$ is an ideal $\mathfrak{b}$ in R. Now, by hypothesis, $\mathfrak{b}$ has a finite basis, say

$$\mathfrak{b} = (b_1, \cdots, b_l),$$

where $b_j \; \varepsilon \; \mathfrak{a}_{k_j}$. If the notation is so chosen that k_l is the largest of the subscripts k_j $(j = 1, 2, \cdots, l)$, it follows that $\mathfrak{b} \subseteq \mathfrak{a}_{k_l}$. But clearly $\mathfrak{a}_{k_l} \subseteq \mathfrak{b}$, so that $\mathfrak{b} = \mathfrak{a}_{k_l}$, and all the $\mathfrak{a}_i$ are contained in $\mathfrak{a}_{k_l}$. Thus we can not have an infinite ascending chain of ideals, and hence $\mathfrak{A}$ contains a maximal element. This shows that (ii) implies (iii).

We complete the proof by showing that (i) is a consequence of (iii). Let $\mathfrak{a}_i$ $(i = 1, 2, \cdots)$ be ideals such that

$$\mathfrak{a}_1 \subseteq \mathfrak{a}_2 \subseteq \cdots.$$

If $\mathfrak{a}_n$ is an ideal which is maximal in this set, then clearly

$$\mathfrak{a}_n = \mathfrak{a}_{n+1} = \mathfrak{a}_{n+2} = \cdots,$$

and the equality holds from some point on.

Emmy Noether (1882–1935) was the first to show the significance of the ascending chain condition (or of the other equivalent conditions) for the ideal theory of a ring. Accordingly, we shall call a ring R a *Noetherian* ring if it is commutative and satisfies the conditions of Theorem 66. Thus, all fields are Noetherian, as is the ring I; while the ring $F[x_1, x_2, \cdots]$ defined above is not Noetherian. In view of condition (ii) of Theorem 66, it is clear that $F[x_1]$ is a Noetherian ring since, according to Theorem 13, every ideal in $F[x_1]$ is principal, that is, has a basis of *one* element. Furthermore, the Boolean ring B of all subsets of the unit interval $\mathcal{I}$ is not Noetherian since there exist ideals in B without a finite basis, as was shown in §12.

We shall now prove the following result of Hilbert:

THEOREM 67. *If the Noetherian ring R has a unit element and x is an indeterminate, then $R[x]$ is a Noetherian ring.*

We shall find a finite basis for the arbitrary ideal $\mathfrak{a}$ in $R[x]$, but first we define some ideals which are associated with the ideal $\mathfrak{a}$.

If f is any nonzero element of $R[x]$, let us denote by f^* the leading coefficient of f, and let $0^* = 0$. We show that the set $\mathfrak{f}$ of all f^* where $f \equiv 0(\mathfrak{a})$ is an ideal in R. Let f and g be any elements of $\mathfrak{a}$, of degrees k and l respectively, and assume for convenience that $k \geq l$. Since R has a unit element, x^{k-l} is an element of $R[x]$ and hence $f - x^{k-l}g$ is in $\mathfrak{a}$. If $f^* \neq g^*$, it follows that

$$f^* - g^* = (f - x^{k-l}g)^*,$$

so that the difference of any two elements of $\mathfrak{f}$ is an element of $\mathfrak{f}$. Also, if $a \ \varepsilon \ R$, $af^* = 0^*$ or $af^* = (af)^* \equiv 0(\mathfrak{f})$. Thus $\mathfrak{f}$ is an ideal in R and hence, by hypothesis, $\mathfrak{f}$ has a finite basis $(a_1, a_2, \cdots, a_\alpha)$. Let f_i denote any fixed element of $\mathfrak{a}$ with leading coefficient a_i ($i = 1, 2, \cdots, \alpha$), and set

$$\mathfrak{b} = (f_1, f_2, \cdots, f_\alpha).$$

Thus $\mathfrak{b}$ is an ideal in $R[x]$, and $\mathfrak{b} \subseteq \mathfrak{a}$.

Now let k be a fixed nonnegative integer. If there exist polynomials in $\mathfrak{a}$ of degree k, the leading coefficients of all these polynomials, together with zero, form an ideal $\mathfrak{m}_k$ in R which therefore has a finite basis, say

$$\mathfrak{m}_k = (b_1, b_2, \cdots, b_{\beta_k}).$$

We let g_{ik} be an element of $\mathfrak{a}$ of degree k with leading coefficient b_i, and set

$$\mathfrak{c}_k = (g_{1k}, g_{2k}, \cdots, g_{\beta_k k}).$$

Thus $\mathfrak{c}_k$ is an ideal in $R[x]$, and clearly $\mathfrak{c}_k \subseteq \mathfrak{a}$. If there exist in $\mathfrak{a}$ no polynomials of degree k, we define $\mathfrak{c}_k = (0)$.

We are now ready to prove the theorem. If n_i denotes the degree of f_i $(i = 1, 2, \cdots, \alpha)$, where the f_i form a basis of $\mathfrak{b}$ as indicated above, and n is the largest of the n_i, we shall show that

(77) $$\mathfrak{a} = (\mathfrak{b}, \mathfrak{c}_{n-1}, \mathfrak{c}_{n-2}, \cdots, \mathfrak{c}_0).$$

Since each of the ideals appearing here is contained in $\mathfrak{a}$, we only need to show that $\mathfrak{a} \subseteq (\mathfrak{b}, \mathfrak{c}_{n-1}, \mathfrak{c}_{n-2}, \cdots, \mathfrak{c}_0)$.

Let f be an element of $\mathfrak{a}$ of degree m and suppose first that $m \geq n$. If $f = ax^m + \cdots$, then $a \equiv 0(\mathfrak{f})$, hence

$$a = \sum_{i=1}^{\alpha} r_i a_i$$

for proper choice of elements r_i in R. It follows that

$$f' = f - \sum_{i=1}^{\alpha} r_i x^{m-n_i} f_i$$

is zero or has degree less than m, and is obviously congruent to f modulo $\mathfrak{b}$. If the degree of f' is as great as n, this process can be repeated. Thus, every element of $\mathfrak{a}$ can be reduced modulo $\mathfrak{b}$ to zero or to a polynomial of degree $\leq n - 1$, and clearly this polynomial will be in $\mathfrak{a}$ since $\mathfrak{b} \subseteq \mathfrak{a}$. Suppose now that

$$g = bx^{n-1} + \cdots, \qquad\qquad (b \neq 0)$$

is an element of $\mathfrak{a}$. Then $b \equiv 0(\mathfrak{m}_{n-1})$, and hence there exist elements s_i of R such that

$$b = \sum_{i=1}^{\beta_{n-1}} s_i b_i.$$

Thus

$$g' = g - \sum_{i=1}^{\beta_{n-1}} s_i g_{i, n-1}$$

is zero or has degree less than $n - 1$, and $g' \equiv 0(\mathfrak{a})$. This shows that every element of $\mathfrak{a}$ of degree $n - 1$ can be reduced modulo c_{n-1} to a polynomial of lower degree, or to zero. In like manner, any element of $\mathfrak{a}$ of degree $n - 2$ can be reduced modulo c_{n-2} to zero or to a polynomial of degree less than $n - 2$. This process can evidently be continued and one therefore finds that any element of $\mathfrak{a}$ is congruent to zero modulo $(\mathfrak{b}, c_{n-1}, c_{n-2}, \cdots, c_0)$. This proves (77) and therefore $\mathfrak{a}$ has a finite basis since each of the ideals $\mathfrak{b}, c_{n-1}, c_{n-2}, \cdots, c_0$ has a finite basis.

By repeated application of this theorem, it is clear that if R is a Noetherian ring with unit element, then $R[x_1, x_2, \cdots, x_n]$ is a Noetherian ring. In particular, $R[x_1, x_2, \cdots, x_n]$ is Noetherian if R is a field or the ring I.

Another method of obtaining Noetherian rings from a given Noetherian ring is indicated by the following theorem:

THEOREM 68. *If $\mathfrak{a}$ is an ideal in the Noetherian ring R, than $R/\mathfrak{a}$ is a Noetherian ring.*

Let $\mathfrak{b}_1, \mathfrak{b}_2, \cdots$ be a sequence of ideals in $R/\mathfrak{a}$ such that

$$\mathfrak{b}_1 \subseteq \mathfrak{b}_2 \subseteq \cdots,$$

and let a_i be the inverse image of b_i under the usual homomorphism $a \to \bar{a}$ of R onto R/a. Then in R we have

$$a_1 \subseteq a_2 \subseteq \cdots,$$

so that for some n we must have $a_n = a_{n+1} = \cdots$. It then follows that $b_n = b_{n+1} = \cdots$, and R/a is necessarily Noetherian.

The next theorem will show how the Noetherian rings fit into the previous theory of this chapter.

THEOREM 69. *In a Noetherian ring R every ideal can be represented as the intersection of a finite number of primary ideals.*

The proof will be accomplished by establishing two lemmas. Before stating the first one, we need one further definition. Let a be an ideal in R. If b and c are ideals in R such that

(78) $\qquad a = b \cap c, \qquad a \subset b, \qquad a \subset c,$

then a is said to be *reducible*. If no ideals b and c exist satisfying these conditions, then a is *irreducible*. Obviously, R itself is an irreducible ideal. Also a prime ideal is necessarily irreducible. For if (78) holds and b is an element of b which is not in a, c an element of c which is not in a, then bc is in both b and c and hence in a. Thus a cannot be prime.

LEMMA 1. *In a Noetherian ring every ideal can be represented as the intersection of a finite number of irreducible ideals.*

Suppose this is false. Then, among the set of ideals which can not be so represented, there is a maximal one, m. Clearly m must be reducible, and thus there exist ideals b and c such that

$$m = b \cap c, \qquad m \subset b, \qquad m \subset c.$$

Because of the maximal property of $\mathfrak{m}$, both $\mathfrak{b}$ and $\mathfrak{c}$ must be representable as the intersection of a finite number of irreducible ideals, say

$$\mathfrak{b} = \mathfrak{b}_1 \cap \mathfrak{b}_2 \cap \cdots \cap \mathfrak{b}_r,$$

and

$$\mathfrak{c} = \mathfrak{c}_1 \cap \mathfrak{c}_2 \cap \cdots \cap \mathfrak{c}_s,$$

where all $\mathfrak{b}_i$ and $\mathfrak{c}_j$ are irreducible. It follows that

$$\mathfrak{m} = \mathfrak{b}_1 \cap \mathfrak{b}_2 \cap \cdots \cap \mathfrak{b}_r \cap \mathfrak{c}_1 \cap \mathfrak{c}_2 \cap \cdots \cap \mathfrak{c}_s,$$

in violation of the fact that $\mathfrak{m}$ has no representation as the intersection of a finite number of irreducible ideals. This contradiction proves Lemma 1.

LEMMA 2. *In a Noetherian ring R, every irreducible ideal is primary.*

We shall prove this by showing that an ideal $\mathfrak{a}$ which is not primary is necessarily reducible.

Since $\mathfrak{a}$ is not primary there exist elements c, d of R such that

$$cd \equiv 0(\mathfrak{a}), \qquad c \not\equiv 0(\mathfrak{a}), \qquad d^i \not\equiv 0(\mathfrak{a}), \quad (i = 1, 2, \cdots).$$

Now the set of all elements x of R such that $xd^i \equiv 0(\mathfrak{a})$ is an ideal $\mathfrak{c}_i$, and clearly

$$\mathfrak{c}_1 \subseteq \mathfrak{c}_2 \subseteq \cdots.$$

Thus, since R is a Noetherian ring, for some positive integer n we must have $\mathfrak{c}_n = \mathfrak{c}_{n+1}$.

Now let $\mathfrak{b}$ be the ideal consisting of all elements of the form

$$rd^n \qquad\qquad (r \ \varepsilon \ R).$$

Clearly, $\mathfrak{a} \subset (\mathfrak{a}, \mathfrak{b})$ since $\mathfrak{b}$ contains d^{n+1} which is not in $\mathfrak{a}$. Also, $\mathfrak{a} \subset (\mathfrak{a}, c)$ since c is not in $\mathfrak{a}$. We shall show that

(79) $$\mathfrak{a} = (\mathfrak{a}, c) \cap (\mathfrak{a}, \mathfrak{b}),$$

from which it will follow that $\mathfrak{a}$ is reducible. It is obvious that we only need to show that any element b in both $(\mathfrak{a}, c)$ and $(\mathfrak{a}, \mathfrak{b})$ is in $\mathfrak{a}$. Since $cd \equiv 0(\mathfrak{a})$, we see that the product of any element of $(\mathfrak{a}, c)$ by d is in $\mathfrak{a}$; thus $bd \equiv 0(\mathfrak{a})$. Since b is also in $(\mathfrak{a}, \mathfrak{b})$ it is expressible in the form

$$(80) \qquad b = a + rd^n,$$

where $a \ \varepsilon \ \mathfrak{a}, r \ \varepsilon \ R$; and thus

$$bd = ad + rd^{n+1} \equiv 0(\mathfrak{a}).$$

It follows that

$$rd^{n+1} \equiv 0(\mathfrak{a}),$$

and since $c_{n+1} = c_n$, we see that

$$rd^n \equiv 0(\mathfrak{a}).$$

Equation (80) then shows that $b \equiv 0(\mathfrak{a})$ as required. This proves Lemma 2 and completes the proof of the theorem.

In view of this theorem, the conclusions of Theorems 64 and 65 are valid for any ideal in a Noetherian ring. We now mention a special case for which we shall find an application in the following section.

We call an ideal in R a *radical ideal* if it coincides with its radical. In view of Theorem 24, a radical ideal $\mathfrak{b}$ is the intersection of the minimal prime ideals belonging to $\mathfrak{b}$. If, in particular, R is a Noetherian ring, Theorems 69 and 60 show that there are only a finite number of these minimal prime ideals, and thus we have

$$\mathfrak{b} = \mathfrak{p}_1 \cap \mathfrak{p}_2 \cap \cdots \cap \mathfrak{p}_k.$$

However, since no one of these prime ideals contains another, this is a short representation of $\mathfrak{b}$ as the intersection of primary (actually prime) ideals. Furthermore, each of these prime ideals is an isolated primary component of $\mathfrak{b}$ and from Theorem 65 we have

THEOREM 70. *In a Noetherian ring every radical ideal has a unique irredundant representation as the intersection of a finite number of prime ideals.*

46. **Ideals and algebraic manifolds.** One of the most interesting and important applications of ideal theory is to be found in the study of algebraic geometry. We shall indicate how ideals come naturally into the theory, and give a very brief account of a few elementary results.

For simplicity of statement and notation, we shall restrict attention to the ring $F[x, y, z]$ of polynomials in three indeterminates with coefficients in the field F of *complex numbers*. Actually, any finite number of indeterminates may just as well be used and with suitable modifications, to be presently described, the field of complex numbers may be replaced by any field.

Consider now a finite system of equations

$$(81) \qquad f_i(x, y, z) = 0 \qquad (i = 1, 2, \cdots, r),$$

where the $f_i(x, y, z)$ are elements of $F[x, y, z]$. By a *solution* (ξ, η, ζ) of this system of equations, we mean that ξ, η, ζ are complex numbers* such that

$$f_i(\xi, \eta, \zeta) = 0 \quad (i = 1, 2, \cdots, r).$$

It is natural to consider a solution (ξ, η, ζ) of these equations as the coordinates of a point in three-dimensional

---

* If F were taken as an arbitrary field it would be necessary (particularly in the proof of Theorem 74) to consider solutions not necessarily in F but which are *algebraic over* F in the sense that each of ξ, η, ζ satisfies some finite algebraic equation with coefficients in F. With this understanding, all the theory of this section is valid for an arbitrary field F. However, the theory is particularly simple for the complex field since, by the "Fundamental Theorem of Algebra," any quantity which is algebraic over the field of complex numbers is itself a complex number.

space. Although the language of ordinary real geometry will be used, it should be remembered that we are actually dealing with a geometry in which the coordinates of a point are complex numbers.

The set N of all points whose coordinates are solutions of a system of equations such as (81) is called an *algebraic manifold* or simply a *manifold*. Clearly, lines and planes are manifolds, as are also all surfaces and curves which can be defined by one or more equations of the form (81).

Now the system of equations defining a given manifold N is certainly not unique. For example, a given line may be obtained as the intersection of many different pairs of planes. However, if we consider the set of *all* elements $f(x, y, z)$ of $F[x, y, z]$ which vanish at all points of N, it is clear that this is an ideal in $F[x, y, z]$ which is uniquely determined by N. We shall call this ideal *the ideal of N*, and denote it by $I(N)$.

Let us now consider an arbitrary ideal $\mathfrak{a}$ in $F[x, y, z]$. By Theorem 67, $\mathfrak{a}$ has a finite basis, say

$$\mathfrak{a} = (g_1, g_2, \cdots, g_n).$$

If N_1 is the manifold defined by

$$g_i(x, y, z) = 0 \qquad (i = 1, 2, \cdots, n),$$

it is clear that all elements of $\mathfrak{a}$, being expressible in the form

$$g_1 h_1 + g_2 h_2 + \cdots + g_n h_n,$$

vanish at all points of N_1. Thus the set of all points at which all elements of the ideal $\mathfrak{a}$ vanish is an algebraic manifold which we call *the manifold of $\mathfrak{a}$*, and denote by $M(\mathfrak{a})$. It will now be clear that every manifold is the manifold of some ideal since the manifold N defined by the equations (81) is just the manifold of the ideal

$(f_1, f_2, \cdots, f_r)$. Thus any manifold is of the form $M(\mathfrak{a})$ for proper choice of the ideal $\mathfrak{a}$. In particular, a single point (ξ_1, η_1, ζ_1) is obviously the manifold of the ideal $(x - \xi_1, y - \eta_1, z - \zeta_1)$. The manifold of the zero ideal is the entire three-dimensional space, while the manifold of the ideal $F[x, y, z]$ is the void set.

From the above definitions, it is easy to see that if $\mathfrak{a} \subseteq \mathfrak{b}$ then $M(\mathfrak{a}) \supseteq M(\mathfrak{b})$. Also, if $N_1 \subseteq N_2$ it follows that $I(N_1) \supseteq I(N_2)$. Furthermore, if $\mathfrak{a}$ is an arbitrary ideal in $F[x, y, z]$, we have $\mathfrak{a} \subseteq I(M(\mathfrak{a}))$ and $M(\mathfrak{a}) = M(I(M(\mathfrak{a})))$. In general, $\mathfrak{a}$ need not coincide with $I(M(\mathfrak{a}))$. As a simple example, let $\mathfrak{a} = (x, y^2)$, in which case $M(\mathfrak{a})$ is just the z-axis. However, $I(M(\mathfrak{a}))$ is the ideal (x, y) which properly contains $\mathfrak{a}$. This example shows that we may have $M(\mathfrak{c}) = M(\mathfrak{b})$ with $\mathfrak{c} \subset \mathfrak{b}$.

THEOREM 71. *If $\mathfrak{r}$ is the radical of the ideal $\mathfrak{a}$ in $F[x, y, z]$, then $M(\mathfrak{a}) = M(\mathfrak{r})$.*

Since $\mathfrak{a} \subseteq \mathfrak{r}$, we have $M(\mathfrak{a}) \supseteq M(\mathfrak{r})$. Let m be any point of $M(\mathfrak{a})$, and g any element of $\mathfrak{r}$. Then, for some $i, g^i \equiv 0(\mathfrak{a})$, hence g^i vanishes at m, and therefore g vanishes at m. Thus all elements of $\mathfrak{r}$ vanish at all points of $M(\mathfrak{a})$; hence $M(\mathfrak{r}) \supseteq M(\mathfrak{a})$. We have therefore shown that $M(\mathfrak{a}) = M(\mathfrak{r})$.

COROLLARY. *If $\mathfrak{p}$ is the prime ideal belonging to the primary ideal $\mathfrak{q}$, then $M(\mathfrak{q}) = M(\mathfrak{p})$.*

We now prove

THEOREM 72. *If $\mathfrak{a}$ and $\mathfrak{b}$ are arbitrary ideals in $F[x, y, z]$, then $M(\mathfrak{a} \cap \mathfrak{b})$ is the union of $M(\mathfrak{a})$ and $M(\mathfrak{b})$; and $M(\mathfrak{a}, \mathfrak{b})$ is the intersection of $M(\mathfrak{a})$ and $M(\mathfrak{b})$.*

Since $\mathfrak{a} \cap \mathfrak{b} \subseteq \mathfrak{a}$, it follows that $M(\mathfrak{a} \cap \mathfrak{b}) \supseteq M(\mathfrak{a})$. Likewise, $M(\mathfrak{a} \cap \mathfrak{b}) \supseteq M(\mathfrak{b})$, and hence $M(\mathfrak{a} \cap \mathfrak{b})$ contains the union of $M(\mathfrak{a})$ and $M(\mathfrak{b})$. Conversely, let m be a point of $M(\mathfrak{a} \cap \mathfrak{b})$. If m were in neither $M(\mathfrak{a})$ nor $M(\mathfrak{b})$ there would exist elements f of $\mathfrak{a}$ and g of $\mathfrak{b}$, neither of which vanishes at m. However, this is impossible since $fg \; \varepsilon \; \mathfrak{a} \cap \mathfrak{b}$, and hence fg vanishes at m, from which it follows that f or g must vanish at m. Hence m must be in the union of $M(\mathfrak{a})$ and $M(\mathfrak{b})$, and this proves the first part of the theorem.

Now $M(\mathfrak{a}, \; \mathfrak{b}) \subseteq M(\mathfrak{a})$ and $M(\mathfrak{a}, \; \mathfrak{b}) \subseteq M(\mathfrak{b})$ since $(\mathfrak{a}, \; \mathfrak{b}) \supseteq \mathfrak{a}$, $(\mathfrak{a}, \; \mathfrak{b}) \supseteq \mathfrak{b}$. This shows that $M(\mathfrak{a}, \; \mathfrak{b})$ is contained in the intersection of $M(\mathfrak{a})$ and $M(\mathfrak{b})$. Conversely, let m be any point of this intersection. Since all elements of $\mathfrak{a}$ and $\mathfrak{b}$ vanish at m, it follows that all elements of $(\mathfrak{a}, \; \mathfrak{b})$, being of the form

$$f + g \qquad\qquad (f \; \varepsilon \; \mathfrak{a}, \; g \; \varepsilon \; \mathfrak{b}) $$

also vanish at m. Hence m is in $M(\mathfrak{a}, \; \mathfrak{b})$, and the proof is completed.

A manifold N which can be expressed as the union of two manifolds N_1 and N_2 with $N_1 \subset N$, $N_2 \subset N$, is said to be *reducible*; otherwise it is *irreducible*.

THEOREM 73. *A manifold N is irreducible if and only if $I(N)$ is a prime ideal.*

First, suppose that N is reducible and is the union of N_1 and N_2 with $N_1 \subset N$, $N_2 \subset N$. If n_1 and n_2 are points of N which are not in N_1 and N_2 respectively, there must exist an element f of $I(N_1)$ which does not vanish at n_1 ; and an element g of $I(N_2)$ which does not vanish at n_2 . Clearly fg then vanishes at all points of N_1 and at all points of N_2 , hence at all points of their union. Thus $fg \equiv 0(I(N))$, and since f does not vanish at n_1 , $f \not\equiv 0(I(N))$. Similarly, $g \not\equiv 0(I(N))$, and therefore $I(N)$ is not prime.

Now let N be irreducible, and suppose that

$$fg \equiv 0(I(N)), \qquad f \not\equiv 0(I(N)). $$

Let us set $N_1 = M(I(N), f)$. Since f does not vanish at all points of N, it is clear that $N_1 \subset N$. If we set $N_2 = M(I(N), g)$, then clearly $N_2 \subseteq N$. Now fg vanishes at any point n of N, hence either f or g vanishes at n; and from this it follows that n is in either N_1 or N_2. Hence N is the union of N_1 and N_2. Since N is assumed to be irreducible we must have $N_2 = N$, which implies that g vanishes at all points of N and therefore $g \equiv 0(I(N))$. This shows that $I(N)$ is prime and completes the proof of the theorem.

We shall presently consider the problem of expressing a given manifold as the union of irreducible manifolds but first we need a more perfect characterization of the irreducible manifolds. The last theorem shows that each irreducible manifold is the manifold of some prime ideal. Actually, the manifold of *every* prime ideal is irreducible. Lack of space prevents us from giving a proof of this fact but we shall state, without proof, the following well-known theorem of Hilbert from which our desired result is easily obtained.

THEOREM 74. *If the polynomial f vanishes at all points of $M(\mathfrak{a})$, then, for some positive integer i, $f^i \equiv 0(\mathfrak{a})$.*

From this, we get the following corollaries:

COROLLARY 1. *If $\mathfrak{a}$ is any ideal in $F[x, y, z]$, $I(M(\mathfrak{a}))$ is the radical of $\mathfrak{a}$.*

COROLLARY 2. *If $\mathfrak{p}$ is a prime ideal, $I(M(\mathfrak{p})) = \mathfrak{p}$, and $M(\mathfrak{p})$ is irreducible.*

Corollary 1 follows immediately from the definition of radical of an ideal; while Corollary 2 is a consequence of the fact that a prime ideal is its own radical, and Theorem 73.

COROLLARY 3. *If $\mathfrak{r}_1$, $\mathfrak{r}_2$ are respectively the radicals of the ideals $\mathfrak{a}_1$, $\mathfrak{a}_2$, then $M(\mathfrak{a}_1) \subseteq M(\mathfrak{a}_2)$ if and only if $\mathfrak{r}_1 \supseteq \mathfrak{r}_2$.*

If $M(\mathfrak{a}_1) \subseteq M(\mathfrak{a}_2)$, then Corollary 1 implies that

$$\mathfrak{r}_1 = I(M(\mathfrak{a}_1)) \supseteq I(M(\mathfrak{a}_2)) = \mathfrak{r}_2 \,.$$

Conversely, if $\mathfrak{r}_1 \supseteq \mathfrak{r}_2$ it is obvious that $M(\mathfrak{r}_1) \subseteq M(\mathfrak{r}_2)$, and thus $M(\mathfrak{a}_1) \subseteq M(\mathfrak{a}_2)$ since the manifold of an ideal coincides with the manifold of its radical.

Since the manifold of any ideal is the manifold of its radical and the radical of any ideal is a radical ideal, every manifold is the manifold of a radical ideal. Furthermore, from Corollary 1 it is clear that radical ideals coincide if and only if they have the same manifold. We have thus established the following result:

COROLLARY 4. *There is a one-to-one correspondence between manifolds and radical ideals.*

As will be indicated in the references below, the next theorem can be established in an elementary fashion without use of ideal theory. However, we shall give a proof based on our Theorem 70.

THEOREM 75. *Every manifold can be uniquely expressed as the union of a finite number of irreducible manifolds no one of which is contained in the union of the others.*

Let N be an arbitrary manifold, and consider the radical ideal $I(N)$. By Theorem 70, we have a unique irredundant representation of $I(N)$ as the intersection of prime ideals,

$$I(N) = \mathfrak{p}_1 \cap \mathfrak{p}_2 \cap \cdots \cap \mathfrak{p}_k \,.$$

Theorem 72 then shows that N is the union of the irreducible manifolds $M(\mathfrak{p}_i)$, $(i = 1, 2, \cdots, k)$. If, for example, $M(\mathfrak{p}_1)$ were contained in the union of the $M(\mathfrak{p}_i)$, $(i = 2, 3, \cdots, k)$, this would imply that $M(\mathfrak{p}_1) \subseteq M(\mathfrak{p}_2 \cap \mathfrak{p}_3 \cap \cdots \cap \mathfrak{p}_k)$. Now the intersection of any number of prime ideals is a radical ideal and Corollary 3 would show that $\mathfrak{p}_1 \supseteq \mathfrak{p}_2 \cap \mathfrak{p}_3 \cap \cdots \cap \mathfrak{p}_k$. However, this would contradict the fact that we have an *irredundant* representation of $I(N)$. Thus $M(\mathfrak{p}_1)$ is not contained in the union of the $M(\mathfrak{p}_i)$, $(i = 2, 3, \cdots, k)$. In like manner, no $M(\mathfrak{p}_j)$ is contained in the union of the $M(\mathfrak{p}_i)$, $(i \neq j)$. This shows that every manifold can be expressed in the desired form.

To show the uniqueness, suppose that N is the union of irreducible manifolds N_i, $(i = 1, 2, \cdots, l)$, it being assumed that no N_j is contained in the union of the others. Then $\mathfrak{p}_i' = I(N_i)$, $(i = 1, 2, \cdots, l)$ are prime ideals, and

$$\mathfrak{p}_1' \cap \mathfrak{p}_2' \cap \cdots \cap \mathfrak{p}_l'$$

is a radical ideal with manifold N; hence must be $I(N)$. Furthermore, no $\mathfrak{p}_j'$ can contain the intersection of the $\mathfrak{p}_i'$, $(i \neq j)$, and therefore this is an irredundant representation of $I(N)$ as the intersection of prime ideals. Hence, by Theorem 70, we must have $k = l$ and, for proper choice of notation, $\mathfrak{p}_i' = \mathfrak{p}_i$ $(i = 1, 2, \cdots, k)$. Thus $N_i = M(\mathfrak{p}_i)$, and the uniqueness is established.

If we start with a given ideal $\mathfrak{a}$ (rather than with a given manifold) whose manifold $M(\mathfrak{a})$ is the N of the above proof, the $\mathfrak{p}_i$ are just the minimal prime ideals belonging to $\mathfrak{a}$. Accordingly, from an irredundant representation of $\mathfrak{a}$ as the intersection of primary ideals we may obtain $M(\mathfrak{a})$ as the union of the manifolds of the minimal among the prime ideals belonging to these primary ideals. As an example, let $\mathfrak{a} = (x^2 + y^2 - 1, x^2 z)$, and thus $M(\mathfrak{a})$ is the set of all points (ξ, η, ζ) whose coordinates satisfy the simultaneous equations

$$x^2 + y^2 - 1 = 0, \qquad x^2 z = 0.$$

It follows that $M(\mathfrak{a})$ consists of the line $x = 0$, $y = 1$; the line $x = 0$, $y = -1$; and the circle $z = 0$, $x^2 + y^2 = 1$. Now it may be shown, although we omit the proof, that

$$\mathfrak{a} = (x^2, y - 1) \cap (x^2, y + 1) \cap (x^2 + y^2 - 1, z),$$

and that this is an irredundant representation of $\mathfrak{a}$ as the intersection of primary ideals. The prime ideals belonging to these primary ideals are respectively $\mathfrak{p}_1 = (x, y - 1)$, $\mathfrak{p}_2 = (x, y + 1)$, $\mathfrak{p}_3 = (x^2 + y^2 - 1, z)$; and since no one of these prime ideals contains another, it is clear that these are the minimal prime ideals belonging to $\mathfrak{a}$. It follows that $M(\mathfrak{a})$ must be the union of $M(\mathfrak{p}_1)$, $M(\mathfrak{p}_2)$, and $M(\mathfrak{p}_2)$. This is readily verified since $M(\mathfrak{p}_1)$ is the line $x = 0, y = 1$; $M(\mathfrak{p}_2)$ is the line $x = 0, y = -1$; and $M(\mathfrak{p}_3)$ is the circle $z = 0$, $x^2 + y^2 = 1$.

REFERENCES

Our discussion of the intersection of primary ideals is based on Krull [2]. See also Bochner [1]. The results, for what we have called Noetherian rings, were first given in Noether [1]. Other proofs are to be found in Krull [1] and van der Waerden [1], Chapter XII. For a proof of Hilbert's Theorem 74, as well as critical discussion of previous proofs, see Zariski [1]. Busemann [1] and Weil [1] are good expositions of the general methods and results of algebraic geometry. Both Busemann [1] and van der Waerden [2] give elementary proofs of our Theorem 75 without use of theorems on the representation of an ideal as the intersection of primary ideals. See also Bochner [1]; Krull [3], [4]; van der Waerden [1], Chapter XIII. For older work on polynomial ideals we may call attention to Macaulay [1] and other references there given.

BIBLIOGRAPHY

Albert, A. A.

[1] *Modern Higher Algebra*, Chicago, 1937.

[2] *Introduction to Algebraic Theories*, Chicago, 1941.

Artin, E., Nesbitt, C. J. and Thrall, R. M.

[1] *Rings with Minimum Condition*, Ann Arbor, 1944.

Birkhoff, G.

[1] *Subdirect unions in universal algebra*, Bull. Amer. Math. Soc., vol. 50 (1944), pp. 764–768.

Birkhoff, G. and MacLane, S.

[1] *A Survey of Modern Algebra*, New York, 1941.

Bochner, S.

[1] *Lectures on Commutative Algebra*, Princeton Univ. Lectures, 1937–38 (Planographed).

Bourbaki, N.

[1] *Éléments de mathématique*. Part I. *Les structures fondamentales de l'analyse*. Livre II. *Algèbre*. Chapitre I. *Structures algébriques* (Actual Sci. Ind., no. 934), Paris, 1942.

Brown, B. and McCoy, N. H.

[1] *Rings with unit element which contain a given ring*. Duke Math. Jour., vol. 13 (1946), pp. 9–20.

[2] *Radicals and subdirect sums*, Amer. Jour. Math., vol. 69 (1947), pp. 46–58.

Busemann, H.

[1] *Introduction to Algebraic Manifolds*, Princeton Univ. Press, 1939 (Planographed).

Dickson, L. E.

[1] *Linear Groups with an Exposition of the Galois Field Theory*, Leipzig, 1901.

[2] *Modern Algebraic Theories*, Chicago, 1926.

Dubreil, P.

[1] *Algèbre*. Vol. 1. *Équivalences, opérations, groupes, anneaux, corps*. (Cahiers scientifiques, no. 20), Paris, 1946.

Forsythe, A.

[1] *Divisors of zero in polynomial rings*, Amer. Math. Monthly, vol. 50 (1943), pp. 7–8.

Forsythe, A. and McCoy, N. H.

[1] *On the commutativity of certain rings*, Bull. Amer. Math. Soc., vol. 52 (1946), pp. 523–526.

Fraenkel, A.

[1] *Über die Teiler der Null und der Zerlegung von Ringen*, Jour. Reine Angew. Math., vol. 145 (1915), pp. 139–176.

Grell, H.

[1] *Beziehungen zwischen Idealen verschiedener Ringe*, Math. Ann., vol. 97 (1927), pp. 490–523.

Halmos, P. R.

[1] *Finite Dimensional Vector Spaces*, Annals of Mathematics Studies, no. 7, Princeton, 1942.

Jacobson, N.

[1] *The Theory of Rings*, New York, 1943.

[2] *The radical and semi-simplicity for arbitrary rings*, Amer. Jour. Math., vol. 67 (1945), pp. 300–320.

[3] *Structure theory for algebraic algebras of bounded degree*, Annals of Math., vol. 46 (1945), pp. 695–707.

Köthe, G.

[1] *Abstrakte Theorie nichtkommutativer Ringe mit einer Anwendung auf die Darstellungstheorie kontinuierlicher Gruppen*, Math. Ann., vol. 103 (1930), pp. 545–572.

Krull, W.

[1] *Ein neuer Beweis für die Hauptsätze der allgemeinen Idealtheorie*, Math. Ann., vol. 90 (1923), pp. 55–64.

[2] *Idealtheorie in Ringen ohne Endlichkeitsbedingung*, Math. Ann., vol. 101 (1929), pp. 729–744.

[3] *Idealtheorie*, Berlin, 1935.

[4] *Enzyklopädie der Mathematischen Wissenschaften* (second edition), vol. I, Part B, *Algebra:*

    I, 1, 11: *Allgemeine Modul-, Ring- und Idealtheorie*,
    I, 1, 12: *Theorie der Polynomideale und Eliminationstheorie*,

Leipzig and Berlin, 1939.

Macaulay, F. S.

[1] *The Algebraic Theory of Modular Systems*, Cambridge Tracts in Mathematics and Mathematical Physics, no. 19, London, 1916.

MacDuffee, C. C.

[1] *The Theory of Matrices*, Berlin, 1933.

[2] *An Introduction to Abstract Algebra*, New York, 1940.

[3] *Vectors and Matrices*, Carus Mathematical Monographs, no. 7, Ithaca, 1943.

McCoy, N. H.

[1] *Subrings of infinite direct sums*, Duke Math. Jour., vol. 4 (1938), pp. 486–494.

[2] *Concerning matrices with elements in a commutative ring*, Bull. Amer. Math. Soc., vol. 45 (1939), pp. 280–284.

[3] *Divisors of zero in matric rings*, Bull. Amer. Math. Soc., vol. 47 (1941), pp. 166–172.

[4] *Remarks on divisors of zero*, Amer. Math. Monthly, vol. 49 (1942), pp. 286–295.

[5] *Subdirectly irreducible commutative rings*, Duke Math. Jour., vol. 12 (1945), pp. 381–387.

[6] *Subdirect sums of rings*, Bull. Amer. Math. Soc., vol. 53 (1947), pp. 856–877.

McCoy, N. H. and Montgomery, D.

[1] *A representation of generalized Boolean rings*, Duke Math. Jour., vol. 3 (1937), pp. 455–459.

von Neumann, J.

[1] *On regular rings*, Proc. Nat. Acad. Sci., vol. 22 (1936), pp. 707–713.

[2] *Continuous Geometry*, Princeton Univ. Lectures, 1936–37 (Planographed)

Noether, E.

[1] *Idealtheorie in Ringbereichen*, Math. Ann., vol. 83 (1921), pp. 24–66.

Stone, M. H.

[1] *The theory of representations for Boolean algebras*, Trans. Amer. Math. Soc., vol. 40 (1936), pp. 37–111..

[2] *The Theory of Real Functions*, Harvard Univ. Lectures, 1940 (Lithoprinted).

Tukey, J. W.

[1] *Convergence and Uniformity in Topology*, Annals of Mathematics Studies, no. 2, Princeton, 1940.

van der Waerden, B. L.

[1] *Moderne Algebra*, vols. 1 and 2, Berlin, 1930 and 1931; 2nd edition, vol. 1, 1937; vol. 2, 1940.

[2] *Algebraische Geometrie*, Berlin, 1939. Reprinted, New York, 1945.

Wedderburn, J. H. M.

[1] *A theorem on finite algebras*, Trans. Amer. Math. Soc., vol. 6 (1905), pp. 349–352.

[2] *Lectures on Matrices*, American Mathematical Society Colloquium Publications, vol. 17, New York, 1934.

Weil, A.

[1] *Foundations of Algebraic Geometry*, American Mathematical Society Colloquium Publications, vol. 29, New York, 1946.

Zariski, O.

[1] *A new proof of Hilbert's Nullstellensatz*, Bull. Amer. Math. Soc., vol. 53 (1947), pp. 362–368.

Zorn, M.

[1] *A remark on method in transfinite algebra,* Bull. Amer. Math. Soc., vol. 41 (1935), pp. 667–670.

INDEX OF TERMS